Working in accounting and finance

Workbook

Michael Fardon

Published by Osborne Books Limited
Unit 1B Everoak Estate
Bromyard Road, Worcester WR2 5HP
Tel 01905 748071
Email books@osbornebooks.co.uk
Website www.osbornebooks.co.uk

Design by Laura Ingham

Printed by CPI Group (UK) Limited, Croydon, CR0 4YY, on environmentally friendly, acid-free paper from managed forests.

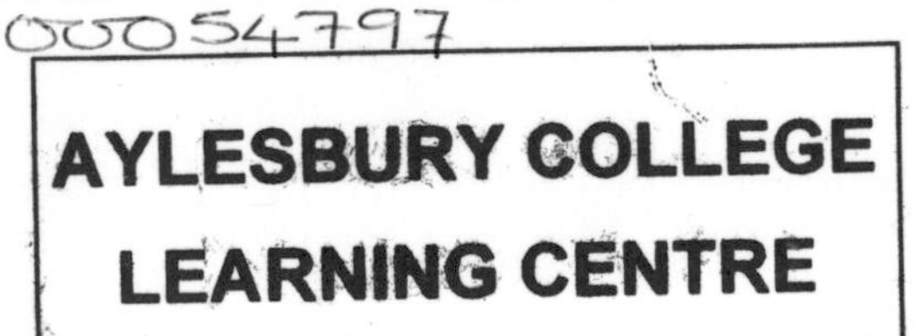

British Library Cataloguing in Publication Data
A catalogue record for this book is available from the British Library

ISBN 978 1909173 088

Contents

Acknowledgements

The publisher wishes to thank Cathy Turner for her help with the reading and production of this book. Thanks are also due to Alison Aplin for her technical reading and Laura Ingham for her designs for this series.

The publisher is indebted to the Association of Accounting Technicians for its help and advice to our authors and editors during the preparation of this text.

Author

Michael Fardon has extensive teaching experience of a wide range of banking, business and accountancy courses at Worcester College of Technology. He now specialises in writing business and financial texts and is General Editor at Osborne Books. He is also an educational consultant and has worked extensively in the areas of vocational business curriculum development.

Introduction

what this book covers

This book has been written to cover the Unit 'Work effectively in accounting and finance' which is mandatory for the revised (2013) AAT Level 2 Certificate in Accounting.

what this book contains

This book is set out in two sections:

- **Chapter Activities** which provide extra practice material in addition to the activities included in the Osborne Books Tutorial text. Answers to the Chapter activities are included in this book.
- **Practice Assessments** are provided to prepare the student for the Computer Based Assessments. They are based directly on the structure, style and content of the sample assessment material provided by the AAT at www.aat.org.uk. Suggested answers to the Practice Assessments are set out in this book.

further information

If you want to know more about our products and resources, please visit www.osbornebooks.co.uk for further details and access to our online shop.

Chapter activities

1 Accounting and finance in the workplace

1.1 The Departments in the list on the left-hand side are provided with accounting information by different sections of the Accounts Department. Match the types of information on the right-hand side with the appropriate Department on the left. Draw lines as appropriate.

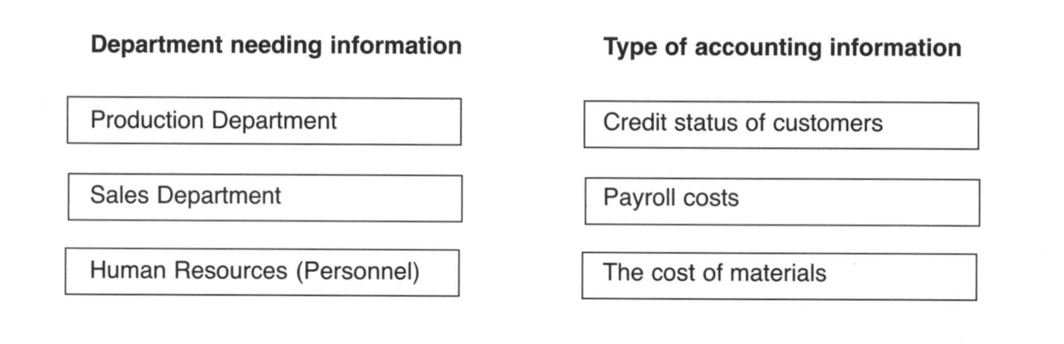

Department needing information	Type of accounting information
Production Department	Credit status of customers
Sales Department	Payroll costs
Human Resources (Personnel)	The cost of materials

1.2 There are three main types of accountant. Match the types of activity listed on the right-hand side with the appropriate type of accountant on the left. Draw lines as appropriate.

Type of accountant	What the job involves
Financial accountant	Checking on financial procedures
Management accountant	Reporting past financial performance
Auditor	Preparing financial forecasts

1.3 Which of the following accounting tasks is **not** part of the costing function? Choose **ONE** option.

	✔
calculating the cost of products	
recording production data such as hours worked	
preparing sales reports for management	
preparing production reports for management	

1.4 Which of the following accounting tasks is part of the purchasing function in a business? Choose **ONE** option.

	✔
recording customer orders, issuing invoices, receiving credit notes	
recording orders made by the business, receiving invoices, receiving credit notes	
recording orders made by the business, issuing invoices, receiving credit notes	
recording customer orders, issuing invoices, issuing credit notes	

1.5 The three people listed in the left-hand column of the table below work for Timon Limited:

Tommy Wong (Accounts Manager)	
Anna Graniello (Chief Cashier)	
David Schofield (Payroll Assistant)	

Enter in the right-hand column the person to whom they are most likely to report.

Choose this person from the following list:

Managing Director

Finance Director

Payroll Line Manager

Accounts Manager

Sales Supervisor

Costing Manager

1.6 An Accounts Assistant working in the Costing Section of a business will report to (indicate the correct option):

	✔
the Costing Manager only	
the Costing Manager and Production Manager only	
the Costing Manager and Production Manager and appropriate people in other Departments of the business	

2 Efficiency and regulation in the workplace

2.1 Organisational policies and procedures are defined as (choose **ONE** option):

	✔
regulations imposed by law which must be adopted by an organisation	
regulations set up by an organisation which must be adopted by that organisation	
the terms relating to the sales of goods and services by an organisation	
a contract of employment issued by an organisation	

2.2 Which **TWO** of the following policies and procedures are most likely to be relevant to the accounting function?

	✔
health and safety at work	
payroll confidentiality guidelines	
quality control in manufacture	
guidance for lifting of heavy packages	

2.3 Identify which of the following will encourage the smooth running of an organisation and which will make no difference to its efficiency. Tick the appropriate column for each line.

	Improves smooth running ✔	**Makes no difference** ✔
A Disciplinary Procedures document		
A 'green' policy of recycling paper		
A staff holiday plan to even out absences		
A manual of accounting procedures		
A weekly fire evacuation drill		

2.4 Identify which of the following will help the solvency of an organisation and which are required for legal compliance reasons. Tick the appropriate column for each line.

	Solvency ✔	**Legal compliance** ✔
Paying employee income tax deductions to HMRC		
Avoiding having to pay overtime to employees		
Making sure credit customers pay up on time		
Completing the VAT Return for HMRC		
Completing the VAT Return on time to avoid a fine		

2.5 Indicate with a tick in the appropriate column below which aspect of running a business best describes the activities listed in the left-hand column. Choose from:

(a) ensuring the smooth running of a business

(b) improving the solvency of a business

(c) compliance with legal requirements by the business

	smooth running ✔	**improving solvency** ✔	**legal compliance** ✔
Reporting on late payments to suppliers			
Chasing up payments due by customers			
Banking cheques payable to the business promptly			
Carrying out a bank reconciliation statement			
Insuring the company cars			
Paying the National Insurance Contributions of employees to HMRC			

3 Ethical behaviour and sustainability

3.1 Ethical Behaviour

(a) The four situations in the table below illustrate breaches of ethical behaviour in the workplace. You are to complete the table by entering the fundamental principle which is breached in each case. Choose from the following four principles:

confidentiality **objectivity** **equality** **integrity**

SITUATION	PRINCIPLE
A manager finds that he is faced with a conflict of interest: his nephew is on the shortlist for a job and he is on the interviewing panel	
An assistant takes money from the petty cash tin to pay for a taxi fare home and then completes a petty cash voucher stating that it was payment for a customer's taxi	
An employee is overheard at the local gym discussing in a very loud voice the details of a customer's trading terms	
A Line Manager always allows one young male employee time off for playing football, but refuses an older female employee permission to have time off to take her daughter to the dentist	

(b) Identify and tick the **TWO** examples below of a **conflict of interest** in an Accounting Department.

	✔
A Line Manager's next-door neighbour is also a supplier and the neighbour asks the Line Manager to see if he can get some orders placed with the neighbour's company	
An Accounts Assistant has a sister who has just been given a job in the Administration Department of the same company	
An Accounts Manager is a keen supporter of the local 'Green Campaign' political party. The local chairman of the party has asked him if he could help provide the local Green Campaign branch with some sponsorship	

(c) In terms of ethical behaviour in an Accounts Department, the active development of accounting skills and knowledge is known as (tick the correct principle):

	✔
Professional behaviour	
Professional competence and due care	
Professional integrity	

3.2 Sustainability

(a) Identify which **FOUR** of the following are examples of a sustainability policy within an organisation.

	✔
Ensuring that all customers are treated on an equal basis	
Maximising sales to overseas countries	
Recycling paper and packaging materials	
Using low energy light bulbs	
Running the office heating at a very low level all year round	
Promoting a car-sharing scheme	
Restricting the use of the internet at work for social networking	
Providing advisers to attend a local school careers conference	

(b) A policy of sustainability in the workplace can sometimes provide financial benefits to an organisation. Indicate in the table below the **TWO** policies which will help to increase profitability

	✔
A reduction in the use of unnecessary product packaging	
The provision by a retailer of free plastic bags for customers	
The use of fuel-efficient company cars	

4 Working with numbers

4.1 Round the following figures to the nearest whole number:

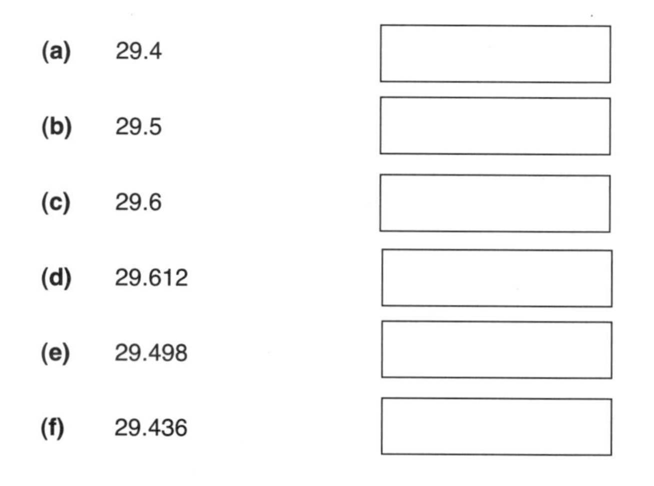

(a) 29.4

(b) 29.5

(c) 29.6

(d) 29.612

(e) 29.498

(f) 29.436

4.2 Round the following figures to two decimal places:

(a) 1.484

(b) 1.445

(c) 1.438

(d) 453.41233

(e) 453.41546

(f) 453.77612

4.3 A fraction, percentage and a ratio are different ways of stating the proportion of parts to a whole, for example the number of female students in an accounting class.

If a class of 18 had 12 females and 6 males, the proportion of females would be:

(a) as a fraction of the class

(b) a percentage of the class rounded to the nearest number

(c) the ratio of females to males in the class

4.4 You ask 40 people to a party but only 10 arrived within the first hour.

Express this number of guests who came as:

(a) a fraction of the people invited

(b) a percentage of the people invited

(c) the ratio of people who came to those who stayed away

Towards the end of the party another 5 guests arrive, saying that their taxi did not turn up on time. No other guests arrived.

Express the final total number of guests at the party as:

(d) a fraction of those invited

(e) a percentage (to one decimal place) of those invited

(f) the ratio of people who came to those who stayed away

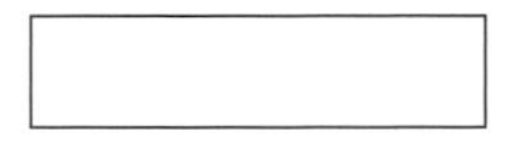

4.5 You are given some receipts to process for petty cash. They include the amount paid but do not show the VAT amount. You are to calculate the VAT content and enter the VAT figure and the net amount (before VAT) in the table below.

	amount on receipt £	VAT amount £	net amount £
(a)	12.00		
(b)	5.76		
(c)	10.74		

4.6 You are asked to add VAT at 20% to the following invoice amounts and calculate **the final total**. No discounts are involved. You should round down the VAT amounts to the nearest pence.

(a) £1,200.50 [ ]

(b) £456.24 [ ]

(c) £12.99 [ ]

4.7 You are issuing three invoices to customers to whom you allow settlement discount at 5%. The invoices also require the addition of VAT at 20%. The amounts shown are the totals after the deduction of trade discount. VAT should be **rounded down** to the nearest pence. Enter the **VAT** and the **final invoice total** of the three invoices in the table below.

	total amount £	VAT charged £	final invoice amount £
(a)	1,250.00		
(b)	495.20		
(c)	845.60		

4.8 You work as an Accounts Assistant for Belloptics Limited, a manufacturer of spectacles and sunglasses.

Your Accounts Manager has asked you to compile and process sales figures for the five Sales Managers who operate in the UK. This is not only so that she can compare their performance but also so that their monthly sales commission of 5% can be calculated.

The sales figures are for a four week period and do **not** include VAT at 20%.

The figures are as follows:

Sales Manager	Week 1 £	Week 2 £	Week 3 £	Week 4 £	Total £
Briggs	5,450	16,975	8,291	13,175	
Lucas	9,632	12,197	3,046	12,316	
Patel	8,705	10,114	9,277	11,207	
Hartmann	7,812	12,093	10,630	12,951	
Ponti	8,361	10,176	12,950	16,230	
Totals					

You are to:

(a) Total the sales for each Sales Manager for Weeks 1 to 4. Enter the figures in the right-hand column of the table.

(b) Total the sales for each week and enter the figures in the bottom row of the table.

(c) Total the four figures in the bottom row and enter the total in the bottom right-hand box of the table.

(d) Now check your accuracy by totalling the first five figures in the right-hand column. This total should be the same as the total in the bottom right-hand box of the table. If there is a difference, you will need to check your workings.

(e) You now need to calculate the commission for each Sales Manager. This is worked out at 5% of the sales figure excluding VAT to the nearest pound.

Enter the sales total in the second column and the commission to be paid in the third column.

Sales Manager	**Total sales** £	**5% Commission due** work to nearest £
Briggs		
Lucas		
Patel		
Hartmann		
Ponti		

(f) Your manager notices that Lucas has included VAT at 20% in his sales figure. This has inflated the figure, which should not contain the VAT charged.

She asks you to recalculate his sales figure by removing the VAT. She suggests the easiest way of doing this is by multiplying the amount including VAT by the 'VAT fraction' of one sixth, ie $^1/_6$, and then recalculating the commission at 5%.

Carry out the calculation and enter your results in the table below. Work to the nearest pence for all the figures, except for the revised commission figure which should be rounded to the nearest pound.

	£
Original amount including VAT	
Minus VAT content (amount x $^1/_6$)	
Correct net sales total for Lucas	
Revised commission at 5%	

(g) Your manager asks you for the amount of the error as she wants to speak to Lucas about it.

The error amounts to: £

5a Communication at work – use of correct grammar

5a.1 Its or It's? Study the four sentences below and tick the **TWO** correct options.

	✔
Its time to study	
It's time to study	
I hate this pasta; I do not like it's taste	
I hate this pasta; I do not like its taste	

5a.2 Its or It's? Study the four sentences below and tick the **TWO** correct options.

	✔
It's been raining non-stop for two weeks	
Its been raining non-stop for two weeks	
I love this carpet; I really like it's colour	
I love this carpet; I really like its colour	

5a.3 Its or It's? Study the four sentences below and tick the **TWO** correct options.

	✔
Its been ages since I saw you	
It's been ages since I saw you	
I like this coffee; it's aroma is very strong	
I like this coffee; its aroma is very strong	

5a.4 Its or It's? Study the four sentences below and tick the **TWO** correct options.

	✔
I like your perfume, its scent reminds me of roses	
I like your perfume, it's scent reminds me of roses	
I am glad I met you; its been a great evening	
I am glad I met you; it's been a great evening	

5a.5 There, their or they're? Study the three sentences below and tick the correct option.

	✔
There are many textbooks available	
Their are many textbooks available	
They're are many textbooks available	

5a.6 There, their or they're? Study the three sentences below and tick the correct option.

	✔
Have the students taken there assessments yet?	
Have the students taken they're assessments yet?	
Have the students taken their assessments yet?	

5a.7 There, their or they're? Study the three sentences below and tick the correct option.

	✔
The students are sure that there competent	
The students are sure that they're competent	
The students are sure that their competent	

5a.8 There, their or they're? Study the three sentences below and tick the correct option.

	✔
It's there problem, not mine!	
It's they're problem, not mine!	
It's their problem, not mine!	

5a.9 Two, too or to? Study the three sentences below and tick the correct option.

	✔
This curry is far two hot for me!	
This curry is far too hot for me!	
This curry is far to hot for me!	

5a.10 Two, too or to? Study the three sentences below and tick the correct option.

	✔
These questions make me go two sleep	
These questions make me go too sleep	
These questions make me go to sleep	

5a.11 Two, too or to? Study the three sentences below and tick the correct option.

	✔
Two much double-entry is bad for your health	
Too much double-entry is bad for your health	
To much double-entry is bad for your health	

5a.12 Two, too or to? Study the three sentences below and tick the correct option.

	✔
Two is company, three is a crowd	
Too is company, three is a crowd	
To is company, three is a crowd	

5b Communication at work – emails and letters

5b.1 Your name is Charlie and you work as an assistant in the Accounts Department of Gerrard Sportsgoods and have been passed the draft email (shown below) to complete.

The email is a request to Ayan Banerjee (a.banerjee@gerrardsportsgoods.com), an assistant in the Production Department, to provide details of 'Anfield' footballs manufactured during the month of July. You need the information by 2 August. You are to:

(a) Insert the email address of the recipient in the appropriate box.

(b) Complete the remaining boxes (they are numbered for reference) with the most appropriate words or phrases from the lists shown below (also numbered for reference).

From c.brooks@gerrardsportsgoods.com

To [ ]

Subject [1]

Hi Ayan

Please send me the quantity of [2] manufactured during the month of [3]. We need this information to carry out a costing exercise. I need the information, please, by [4].

Many thanks and kind regards

Charlie

Accounts Department

Option Lists

Pick one word or phrase for each numbered box from the following numbered lists:

1. Manufacturing data for July, August data, Manufacturing data for August, Footballs
2. footballs, July footballs, 'Anfield' footballs, sports goods
3. May, June, July, August
4. 2 May, August, 2 July, 2 August

5b.2 You have been passed the following draft letter (to a Mrs Clinton) to check.

There are five major errors which could include wrong spellings, bad grammar or wrong use of words.

You are to:

(a) Identify the five incorrect words and enter them in the left-hand column of the table below.

(b) Enter your correction of these five words on the appropriate line in the right-hand column of the table below.

Dear Miss Clinton,

Credit card referral

We have been advised by Worldpay that a purchase for £65.00 made by you on 13 July has been refused by your credit card company.

We recomend that you make a seperate payment to us by cheque or bank transfer so that we can fulfil your order. Their both acceptable methods.

Yours faithfully,

incorrect word	correction

5c Communication at work – reports

5c.1 A business report normally contains seven sections, each with a distinct function. The seven sections are:

Title, Summary, Introduction, Findings, Conclusions, Recommendations, Appendices

You are to match the two sections on the left with the appropriate descriptions on the right. Draw two lines as appropriate.

Section title	Section contents
	A short explanation (often for managers and executives) summarising the areas the report examines.
	This sets out and analyses the results of the investigations of the report.
Recommendations	A single page stating what the report is about, who wrote it, and the date it was written.
	This sets out the information gathered by the report and is the basis for the conclusions.
Conclusions	The suggested course(s) of action which are based on the report.
	Additional information which supports the report but is not contained in the findings.
	This section tells the reader how the report came about and explains the nature of the tasks and the people involved.

5c.2 Ella, the Human Resources Manager at Mercato Limited, has been receiving feedback from staff in the Accounts Department who are becoming dissatisfied with their lack of promotion.

Ella contacts the Accounts Department Manager and they decide to organise a staff survey and a series of interviews to find out about levels of motivation and the need for staff training. The report which they produce will help them in their CPD (Continuing Professional Development) planning and the making of recommendations for the staff.

The results of their investigation are set out in the table below. 50 members of staff were interviewed.

The areas being investigated were graded in three levels: 'Good', 'Fair' and 'Poor'.

RESULTS OF STAFF CPD QUESTIONNAIRE			
Question	**Good**	**Fair**	**Poor**
How do you rate your motivation for doing your current job?	7	23	20
How do you rate the training you are given in your job?	4	22	24
How do you rate your opportunities for promotion?	3	27	20

(a) Convert the figures in the above table to percentages of the total number of responses and complete the table below. Remember that there were 50 members of staff interviewed altogether.

RESULTS OF STAFF CPD QUESTIONNAIRE			
Question	**Good %**	**Fair %**	**Poor %**
How do you rate your motivation for doing your current job?			
How do you rate the training you are given in your job?			
How do you rate your opportunities for promotion?			

(b) Select **TWO conclusions** to be included in the report. Tick the appropriate boxes.

	✔
The results for motivation and promotion opportunities were both excellent	
The result for motivation was less positive than the result for promotion opportunites	
The worst result related to the quality of staff training	
There is no real reason for changing the present training system	
All areas of CPD (motivation, training and promotion) need urgent attention	
Staff seem very happy with the present system of training and promotion	

(c) Select **TWO recommendations** to be included in the report. Tick the appropriate boxes.

	✔
Reduce the number of staff so that there will be more opportunity for individuals to go on training courses	
Review and expand the training programmes so that there is more opportunity for improving staff performance and motivation	
Schedule and carry out CPD interviews with all members of staff so that individual needs are fulfilled and motivation improved	
Reduce the frequency of staff interviews so that they will have less opportunity to complain and get demoralised	

6 Managing your work

6.1 If you find that you are falling seriously behind with your work and cannot meet a deadline you should (choose the most appropriate option):

	✔
Tell your Line Manager	
Not tell your Line Manager	
Tell a colleague that he/she should help you	
Say you have a bad headache and you need to go home	

6.2 In which of the following circumstances are you likely to need to change the priority of your work (choose **ONE** option):

	✔
Your Line Manager asks to you join her in an important meeting	
A colleague has too much work to do and wants you to help	
A colleague tells you that your computer screen will give you eye strain	
There is a fire drill and you have to temporarily evacuate the building	

6.3 Match the planning aid in the left-hand column with the appropriate type of activity in the right-hand column. Draw lines as appropriate.

Planning aid
Schedule
Diary
Chart

Planning activity
A list of activities that have to be done by you
Activities planned for a one day sales conference
A post-it note to remind you to back up the server
Recording future activities for future reference
A visual time line plan for a business project

6.4 Match the planning aid in the left-hand column with the appropriate type of activity in the right-hand column. Draw lines as appropriate.

Planning aid
'To do' list
Action plan
Wall planner

Planning activity
A list of activities that have to be done by you
Activities planned for a one day sales conference
A list of activities to be done by different people
Recording future activities for future reference
A visual time line plan for a business project

6.5 You are a part-time Accounts Assistant employed by Froyd Limited, a printing business. Your main task is to process the payroll, but you also deal with checking incoming payments, preparing payments to suppliers and dealing with petty cash and the petty cash book.

Your working hours are 09.00 to 13.00 Monday to Friday.

You normally attend the weekly staff meeting at 11.00 every Wednesday.

Most employees are salaried and are paid monthly by direct bank transfer (BACS). Their salaries are processed on the last Wednesday of the month and reach their bank account on the last Friday of the month.

Some casual workers have chosen to be paid weekly by BACS and their salaries are processed every Wednesday and reach the bank account every Friday.

Other casual employees are still paid weekly in cash. The payroll for these employees is processed every Wednesday and paid every Friday. One of your jobs is to go to the bank on Thursday to pick up the cash to make up the pay packets for distribution on Friday. At the same time you also pick up from the bank the notes and coins needed to top up the petty cash.

Your normal routine during the week is set out on the schedule below.

Task description	**Scheduling of tasks**		**Time taken for task**
	Day	**Time**	
Process payments received	Monday	9.00	4 hours
Process payments made to suppliers and petty cash payments	Tuesday	9.00	4 hours
Process the payroll (BACS and cash)	Wednesday	9.00	3 hours
Update and balance the petty cash book	Thursday	9.00	2 hour
Visit bank to pick up cash wages and petty cash	Thursday	11.00	1 hour
Lock the cash in the safe and petty cash box	Thursday	12.00	1 hour
Make up cash pay packets and distribute payslips for all employees	Friday	9.00	3 hours

On the last Wednesday in July you and your car are involved in a minor road accident on the way to work. Nobody is hurt but the driver of the other car is not very cooperative and as a result you do not get into the office until 12.00.

The Accounts Manager is very sympathetic as you are a bit shaken up, but he points out that both the weekly and monthly payroll must meet their deadlines as all the staff will need paying on Friday. He suggests that you prioritise what you have to do for the rest of the week. He has agreed to let you work additional hours on Thursday afternoon so that you can ensure that all the tasks are completed.

(a) Using the table below, write a 'to do' list for the rest of Wednesday morning, Thursday and Friday by listing the tasks in order of completion. Write the task descriptions in the column on the right. Choose from the following tasks:

Make up cash pay packets and distribute payslips for all employees

Update and balance the petty cash book

Deal with payments made to suppliers and petty cash payments

Process the payroll (BACS and cash)

Lock the cash in the safe and petty cash box

Visit the bank to pick up cash wages and petty cash top up

Process payments received

WEDNESDAY/THURSDAY/FRIDAY 'TO DO' LIST (in order of completion)	
Task 1	
Task 2	
Task 3	
Task 4	
Task 5	

(b) If you **do not** carry out the instructions of the Accounts Manager there might be problems. Indicate below with a tick in the appropriate column whether the following outcomes could have serious consequences for Froyd Ltd or not.

	serious ✔	**not serious** ✔
The staff may not get paid on time		
The cash from the bank may not get locked away		
Petty cash reimbursements may be delayed		
Suppliers may not get paid on time		
Minor office duties may not get done		

7 Working as a member of an effective team

7.1 If you suspect that your Line Manager is showing favouritism to a colleague at your expense, you should (tick the appropriate option):

	✔
Talk to your colleague about the problem	
Talk to a more senior manager about the problem when you have an appraisal	
Take the matter to an Industrial Tribunal	

7.2 You see that a colleague is stealing small items of stationery such as paper, pens and staplers. You should (tick the appropriate option):

	✔
Ask your colleague why she does it	
Refer it to your Line Manager if it continues	
Replace the items yourself	

7.3 You notice that a colleague is taking short cuts in her invoicing work and not following the normal checking processes set down in the procedures manual. As a result, mistakes are occurring and the whole team is getting the blame. The action you should take is as follows (tick the appropriate option):

	✔
Refer it straight to the Senior Accounts Manager	
Talk to your colleague about it in the first instance, pointing out the errors	
Amend the procedures manual	

7.4 Your Line Manager (an older man) is constantly making sexist remarks to the whole office at the expense of a young female trainee – for example 'You can't expect her to get it right first time, she's had another blonde moment!'

She has expressed her concern by getting very upset and rushing off to the rest-room in tears, but the Line Manager takes no notice.

The appropiate action to be taken is (tick the correct option):

	✔
The trainee should pursue the matter through the Grievance Procedure	
You and your colleagues should organise a petition to the Managing Director	
The police should be called in as the Sex Discrimination Act is involved	

8 CPD – developing skills and knowledge at work

8.1 The order of the main stages in the CPD (Continuing Professional Development) process is:

	✔
Identification of objectives, identification of needs, identification of learning methods, evaluation of success	
Identification of needs, identification of objectives, identification of learning methods, evaluation of success	
Identification of needs, identification of learning methods, identification of objectives, evaluation of success	

8.2 'SMART' objectives in the CPD (Continuing Professional Development) process are (tick the correct option):

	✔
Specific, Measurable, Achievable, Realistic, Timely	
Secure, Meaningful, Accurate, Realistic, Timely	
Safe, Measurable, Accurate, Realistic, Timely	

8.3 Which of the following is **not** part of the normal CPD (Continuing Professional Development) process? Tick the appropriate option.

	✔
Studying for a further qualification	
Progressing to another job with the same employer	
Changing to the same job with a different employer	

8.4 Your manager has recently reviewed your performance and identified your strengths and weaknesses. He has suggested a number of ways in which you can improve your performance (remedying weaknesses) and develop your skills (developing your strengths).

You are to match the strength and the weakness on the left with the appropriate improvement and development opportunities on the right. Draw two lines as appropriate.

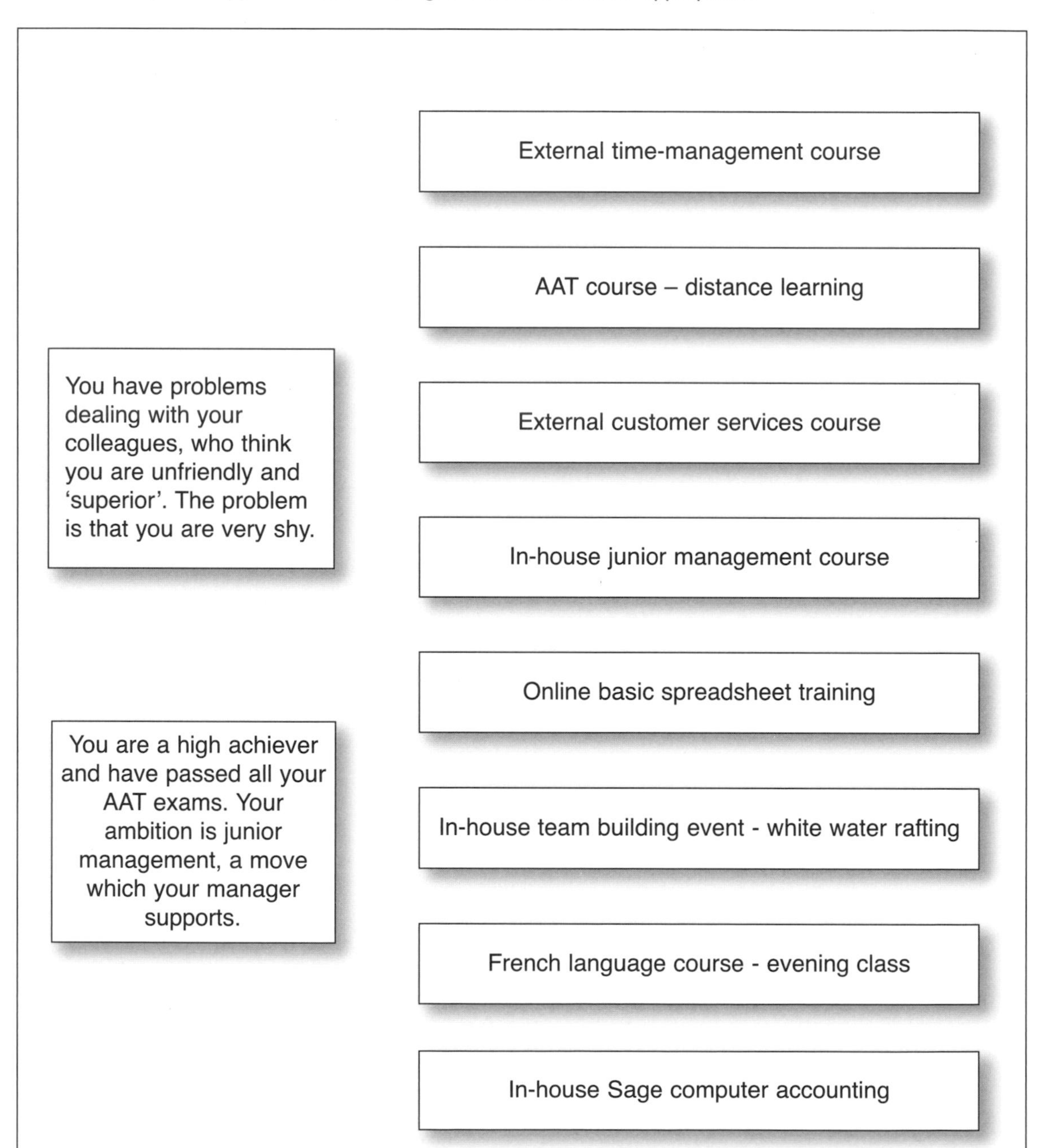

Chapter activities answers

1 Accounting and finance in the workplace

1.1

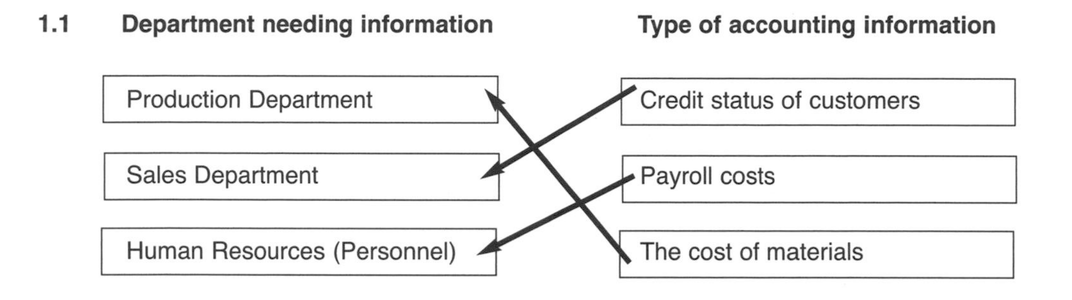

1.2

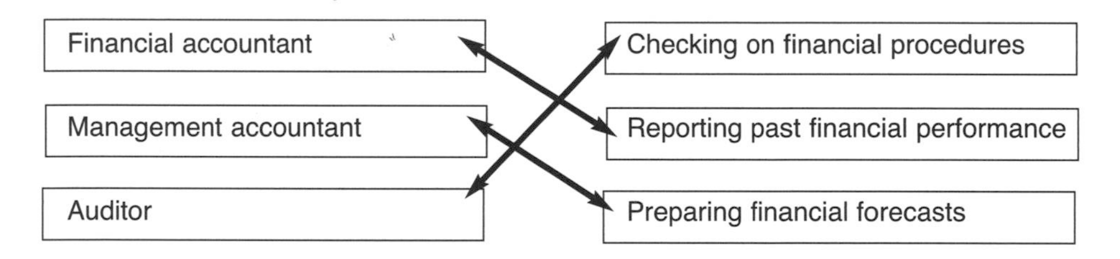

1.3

Calculating the cost of products	
Recording production data such as hours worked	
Preparing sales reports for management	✔
Preparing production reports for management	

1.4

Recording customer orders, issuing invoices, receiving credit notes	
Recording orders made by the business, receiving invoices, receiving credit notes	✔
Recording orders made by the business, issuing invoices, receiving credit notes	
Recording customer orders, issuing invoices, issuing credit notes	

1.5

Tommy Wong (Accounts Manager)	Finance Director
Anna Graniello (Chief Cashier)	Accounts Manager
David Schofield (Payroll Assistant)	Payroll Line Manager

1.6

The Costing Manager only	
The Costing Manager and Production Manager only	
The Costing Manager and Production Manager and appropriate people in other departments of the business	✔

2 Efficiency and regulation in the workplace

2.1

Regulations imposed by law which must be adopted by an organisation	
Regulations set up by an organisation which must be adopted by that organisation	✔
The terms relating to the sales of goods and services by an organisation	
A contract of employment issued by an organisation	

2.2

Health and safety at work	✔
Payroll confidentiality guidelines	✔
Quality control in manufacture	
Guidance for lifting of heavy packages	

2.3

	Improves smooth running	Makes no difference
A Disciplinary Procedures document	✔	
A 'green' policy of recycling paper		✔
A staff holiday plan to even out absences	✔	
A manual of accounting procedures	✔	
A weekly fire evacuation drill		✔

2.4

	Solvency	Legal compliance
Paying employee income tax deductions to HMRC		✔
Avoiding having to pay overtime to employees	✔	
Making sure credit customers pay up on time	✔	
Completing the VAT Return for HMRC		✔
Completing the VAT Return on time to avoid a fine	✔	

2.5

	smooth running	improving solvency	legal compliance
Reporting on late payments to suppliers	✔		
Chasing up payments due by customers		✔	
Banking cheques payable to the business promptly		✔	
Carrying out a bank reconciliation statement	✔		
Insuring the company cars			✔
Paying the National Insurance Contributions of employees to HMRC			✔

3 Ethical behaviour and sustainability

3.1 **(a)**

SITUATION	ETHICAL PRINCIPLE
A manager finds that he is faced with a conflict of interest: his nephew is on the shortlist for a job and he is on the interviewing panel	objectivity
An assistant takes money from the petty cash tin to pay for a taxi fare home and then completes a petty cash voucher stating that it was payment for a customer's taxi	integrity
An employee is overheard at the local gym discussing in a very loud voice the details of a customer's trading terms	confidentiality
A line manager always allows one young male employee time off for playing football, but refuses an older female employee permission to have time off to take her daughter to the dentist	equality

(b)

A line manager's next-door neighbour is also a supplier and the neighbour asks the line manager to see if he can get some orders placed with the neighbour's company	✔
An accounts assistant has a sister who has just been given a job in the administration department of the same company	
An accounts manager is a keen supporter of the local 'Green Campaign' political party. The local chairman of the party has asked him if he could help provide the local Green Campaign branch with some sponsorship	✔

(c)

Professional behaviour	
Professional competence and due care	✔
Professional integrity	

3.2 (a)

Ensuring that all customers are treated on an equal basis	
Maximising sales to overseas countries	
Recycling paper and packaging materials	✔
Using low energy light bulbs	✔
Running the office heating at a very low level all year round	
Promoting a car-sharing scheme	✔
Restricting the use of the internet at work for social networking	
Providing advisers to attend a local school careers conference	✔

(b)

A reduction in the use of unnecessary product packaging	✔
The provision by a retailer of free plastic bags for customers	
The use of fuel-efficient company cars	✔

4 Working with numbers

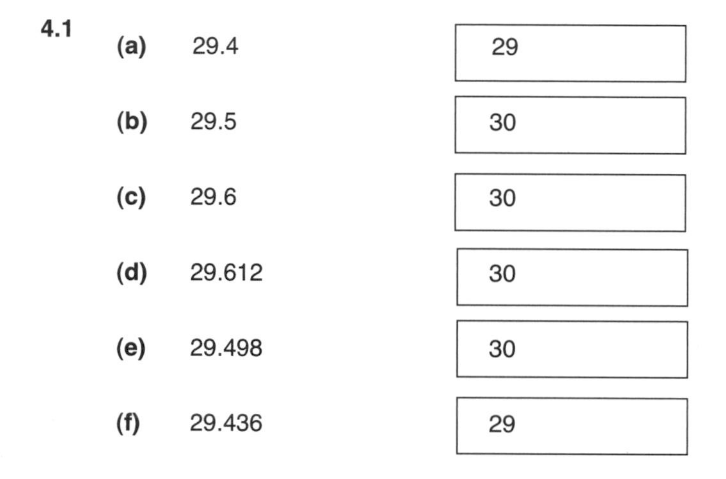

4.1

(a)	29.4	29
(b)	29.5	30
(c)	29.6	30
(d)	29.612	30
(e)	29.498	30
(f)	29.436	29

4.2

(a)	1.484	1.48
(b)	1.445	1.45
(c)	1.438	1.44
(d)	453.41233	453.41
(e)	453.41546	453.42
(f)	453.77612	453.78

4.3

(a) as a fraction of the class — $^{2}/_{3}$ (ie $^{12}/_{18}$)

(b) a percentage of the class rounded to the nearest number

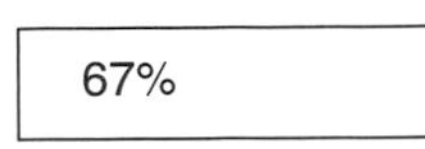

(c) the ratio of females to males in the class

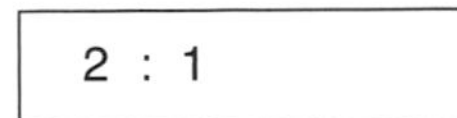

4.4

(a) a fraction of the people invited — $^{1}/_{4}$

(b) a percentage of the people invited — 25%

(c) the ratio of people who came to those who stayed away — 1 : 3

(d) a fraction of those invited

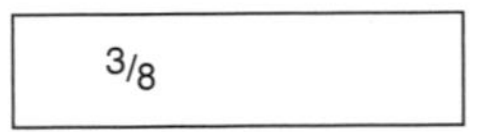

(e) a percentage (to one decimal place) of those invited — 37.5%

(f) the ratio of people who came to those who stayed away — 3 : 5

4.5

	amount on receipt £	VAT amount £	net amount £
(a)	12.00	2.00	10.00
(b)	5.76	0.96	4.80
(c)	10.74	1.79	8.95

4.6

(a) £1,200.50 £1,440.60

(b) £456.24 £547.48

(c) £12.99 £15.58

4.7

	total amount £	VAT charged £	final invoice amount £
(a)	1,250.00	237.50	1487.50
(b)	495.20	94.08	589.28
(c)	845.60	160.66	1,006.26

4.8 (a) to (d)

Sales Manager	Week 1	Week 2	Week 3	Week 4	Total
	£	£	£	£	£
Briggs	5,450	16,975	8,291	13,175	43,891
Lucas	9,632	12,197	3,046	12,316	37,191
Patel	8,705	10,114	9,277	11,207	39,303
Hartmann	7,812	12,093	10,630	12,951	43,486
Ponti	8,361	10,176	12,950	16,230	47,717
Totals	39,960	61,555	44,194	65,879	211,588

(e)

Sales Manager	Total sales	5% Commission due
	£	work to nearest £
Briggs	43,891	2,195
Lucas	37,191	1,860
Patel	39,303	1,965
Hartmann	43,486	2,174
Ponti	47,717	2,386

(f)

	£
Original amount including VAT	37,191.00
Minus VAT content (amount x $^1/_6$)	6,198.50
Correct sales total for Lucas	30,992.50
Revised commission at 5%	1,550.00

(g) The error amounts to £310.00

5a Communication at work – use of correct grammar

5a.1

Its time to study	
It's time to study	✔
I hate this pasta; I do not like it's taste	
I hate this pasta; I do not like its taste	✔

5a.2

It's been raining non-stop for two weeks	✔
Its been raining non-stop for two weeks	
I love this carpet; I really like it's colour	
I love this carpet; I really like its colour	✔

5a.3

Its been ages since I saw you	
It's been ages since I saw you	✔
I like this coffee; it's aroma is very strong	
I like this coffee; its aroma is very strong	✔

5a.4

I like your perfume, its scent reminds me of roses	✔
I like your perfume, it's scent reminds me of roses	
I am glad I met you; its been a great evening	
I am glad I met you; it's been a great evening	✔

5a.5

There are many textbooks available	✔
Their are many textbooks available	
They're are many textbooks available	

5a.6

Have the students taken there assessments yet?	
Have the students taken they're assessments yet?	
Have the students taken their assessments yet?	✔

5a.7

The students are sure that there competent	
The students are sure that they're competent	✔
The students are sure that their competent	

5a.8

It's there problem, not mine!	
It's they're problem, not mine!	
It's their problem, not mine!	✔

5a.9

This curry is far two hot for me!	
This curry is far too hot for me!	✔
This curry is far to hot for me!	

5a.10

These questions make me go two sleep	
These questions make me go too sleep	
These questions make me go to sleep	✔

5a.11

Two much double-entry is bad for your health	
Too much double-entry is bad for your health	✔
To much double-entry is bad for your health	

5a.12

Two is company, three is a crowd	✔
Too is company, three is a crowd	
To is company, three is a crowd	

5b Communication at work – emails and letters

5b.1 (a) and (b)

From c.brooks@gerrardsportsgoods.com

To a.banerjee@gerrardsportsgoods.com

Subject Manufacturing data for July [1]

Hi Ayan

Please send me the quantity of 'Anfield' footballs [2] manufactured during the month of July [3]. We need this information to carry out a costing exercise. I need the information, please, by 2 August [4].

Many thanks and kind regards

Charlie

Accounts Department

5b.2 (a) and (b)

incorrect word	correction
Miss	Mrs
recomend	recommend
seperate	separate
Their	They're – or, better – They are
faithfully	sincerely

5c Communication at work – reports

5c.1

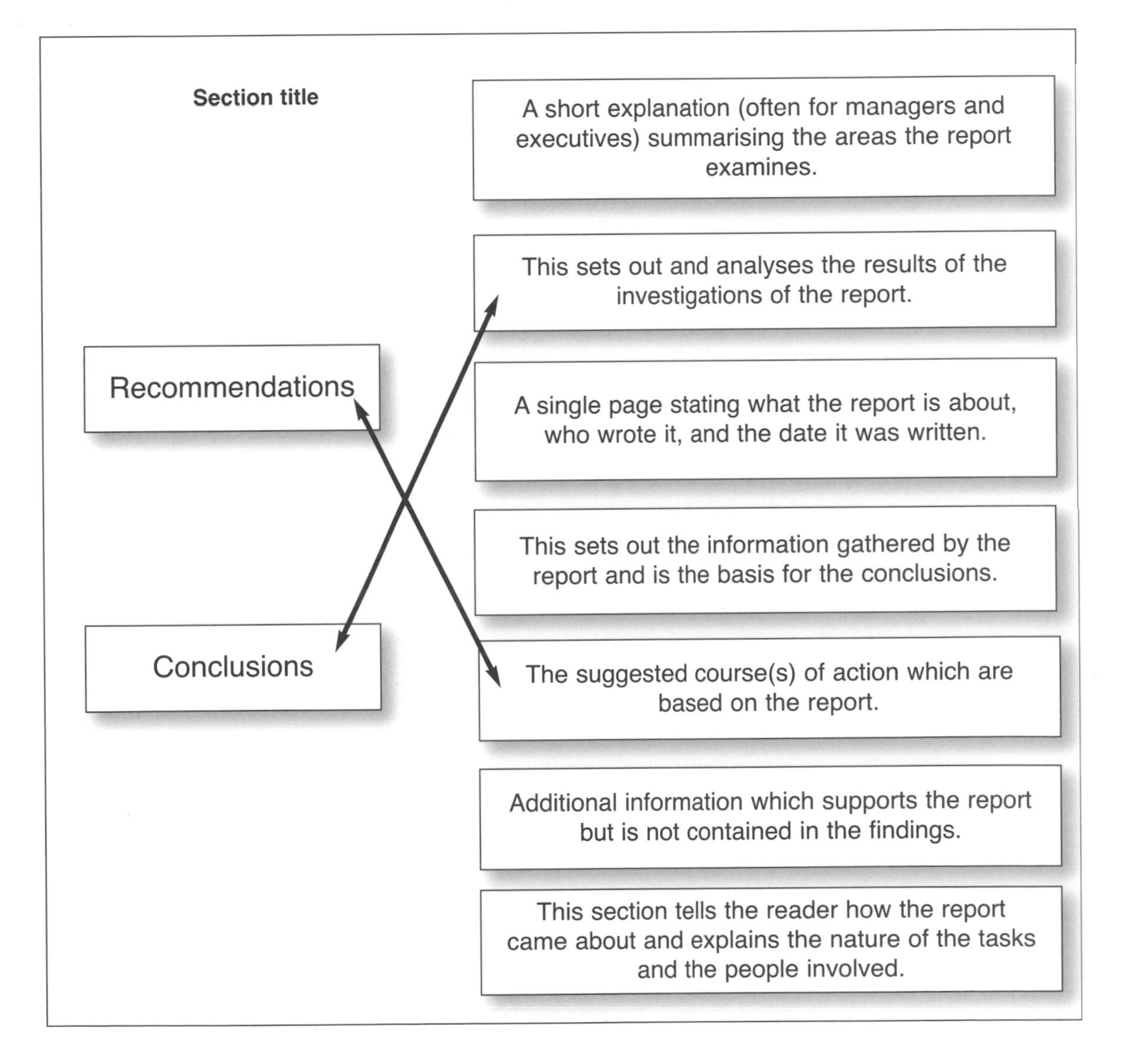

5c.2 (a)

RESULTS OF STAFF CPD QUESTIONNAIRE			
Question	**Good %**	**Fair %**	**Poor %**
How do you rate your motivation for doing your current job?	14	46	40
How do you rate the training you are given in your job?	8	44	48
How do you rate your opportunities for promotion?	6	54	40

(b)

The results for motivation and promotion opportunities were both excellent	
The result for motivation was less positive than the result for promotion opportunites	
The worst result related to the quality of staff training	✔
There is no real reason for changing the present training system	
All areas of CPD (motivation, training and promotion) need urgent attention	✔
Staff seem very happy with the present system of training and promotion	

(c)

Reduce the number of staff so that there will be more opportunity for individuals to go on training courses	
Review and expand the training programmes so that there is more opportunity for improving staff performance and motivation	✔
Schedule and carry out CPD interviews with all members of staff so that individual needs are fulfilled and motivation improved	✔
Reduce the frequency of staff interviews so that they will have less opportunity to complain and get demoralised	

6 Managing your work

6.1

Tell your Line Manager	✔
Not tell your Line Manager	
Tell a colleague that he/she should help you	
Say you have a bad headache and you need to go home	

6.2

Your Line Manager asks to you join her in an important meeting	✔
A colleague has too much work to do and wants you to help	
A colleague tells you that your computer screen will give you eye strain	
There is a fire drill and you have to temporarily evacuate the building	

6.3

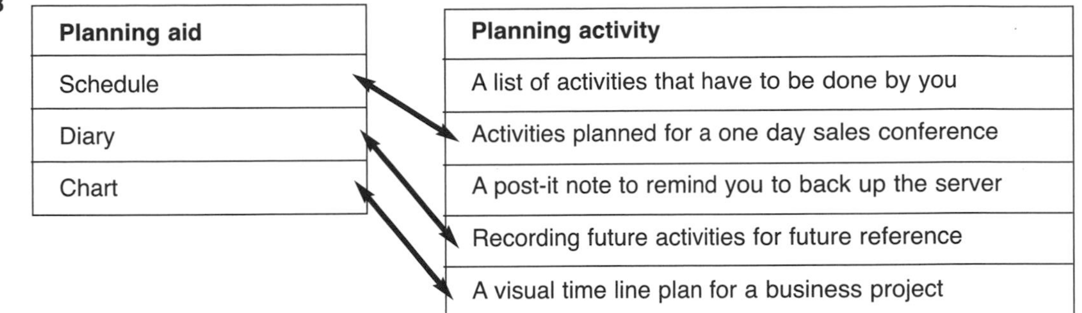
Planning aid
Schedule
Diary
Chart
Planning activity
A list of activities that have to be done by you
Activities planned for a one day sales conference
A post-it note to remind you to back up the server
Recording future activities for future reference
A visual time line plan for a business project

6.4

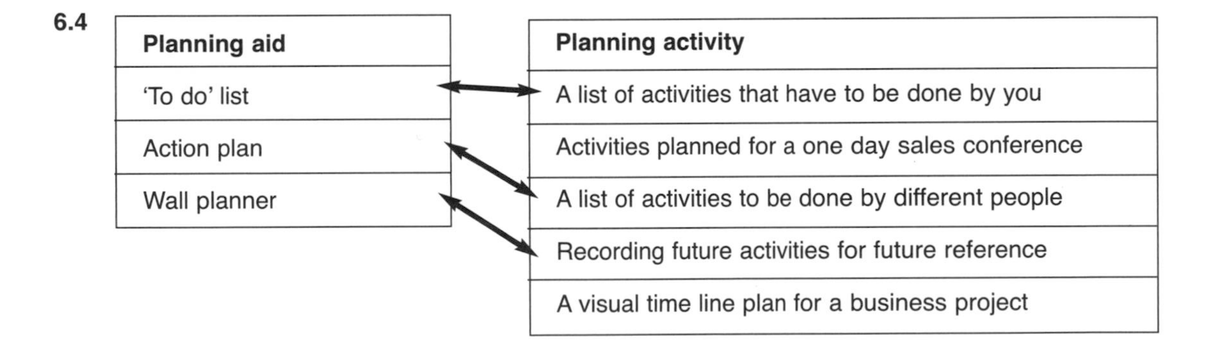
Planning aid
'To do' list
Action plan
Wall planner
Planning activity
A list of activities that have to be done by you
Activities planned for a one day sales conference
A list of activities to be done by different people
Recording future activities for future reference
A visual time line plan for a business project

6.5 (a)

WEDNESDAY/THURSDAY/FRIDAY 'TO DO' LIST (in order of completion)	
Task 1	Process the payroll (BACS and cash)
Task 2	Update and balance the petty cash book
Task 3	Visit the bank to pick up cash wages and petty cash top up
Task 4	Lock the cash in the safe at work
Task 5	Make up cash pay packets and distribute payslips for all employees

(b)

	serious	not serious
The staff may not get paid on time	✔	
The cash from the bank may not get locked away	✔	
Petty cash reimbursements may be delayed		✔
Suppliers may not get paid on time	✔	
Minor office duties may not get done		✔

7 Working as a member of an effective team

7.1

Talk to your colleague about the problem	
Talk to a more senior manager about the problem when you have an appraisal	✔
Take the matter to an Industrial Tribunal	

7.2

Ask your colleague why she does it	
Refer it to your line manager if it continues	✔
Replace the items yourself	

7.3

Refer it straight to the Senior Accounts Manager	
Talk to your colleague about it in the first instance, pointing out the errors	✔
Amend the procedures manual	

7.4

The trainee should pursue the matter through the Grievance Procedure	✔
You and your colleagues should organise a petition to the Managing Director	
The police should be called in as the Sex Discrimination Act is involved	

CPD – developing skills and knowledge at work

8.1

Identification of objectives, identification of needs, identification of learning methods, evaluation of success	
Identification of needs, identification of objectives, identification of learning methods, evaluation of success	✔
Identification of needs, identification of learning methods, identification of objectives, evaluation of success	

8.2

Specific, Measurable, Achievable, Realistic, Timely	✔
Secure, Meaningful, Accurate, Realistic, Timely	
Safe, Measurable, Accurate, Realistic, Timely	

8.3

Studying for a further qualification	
Progressing to another job with the same employer	
Changing to the same job with a different employer	✔

8.4

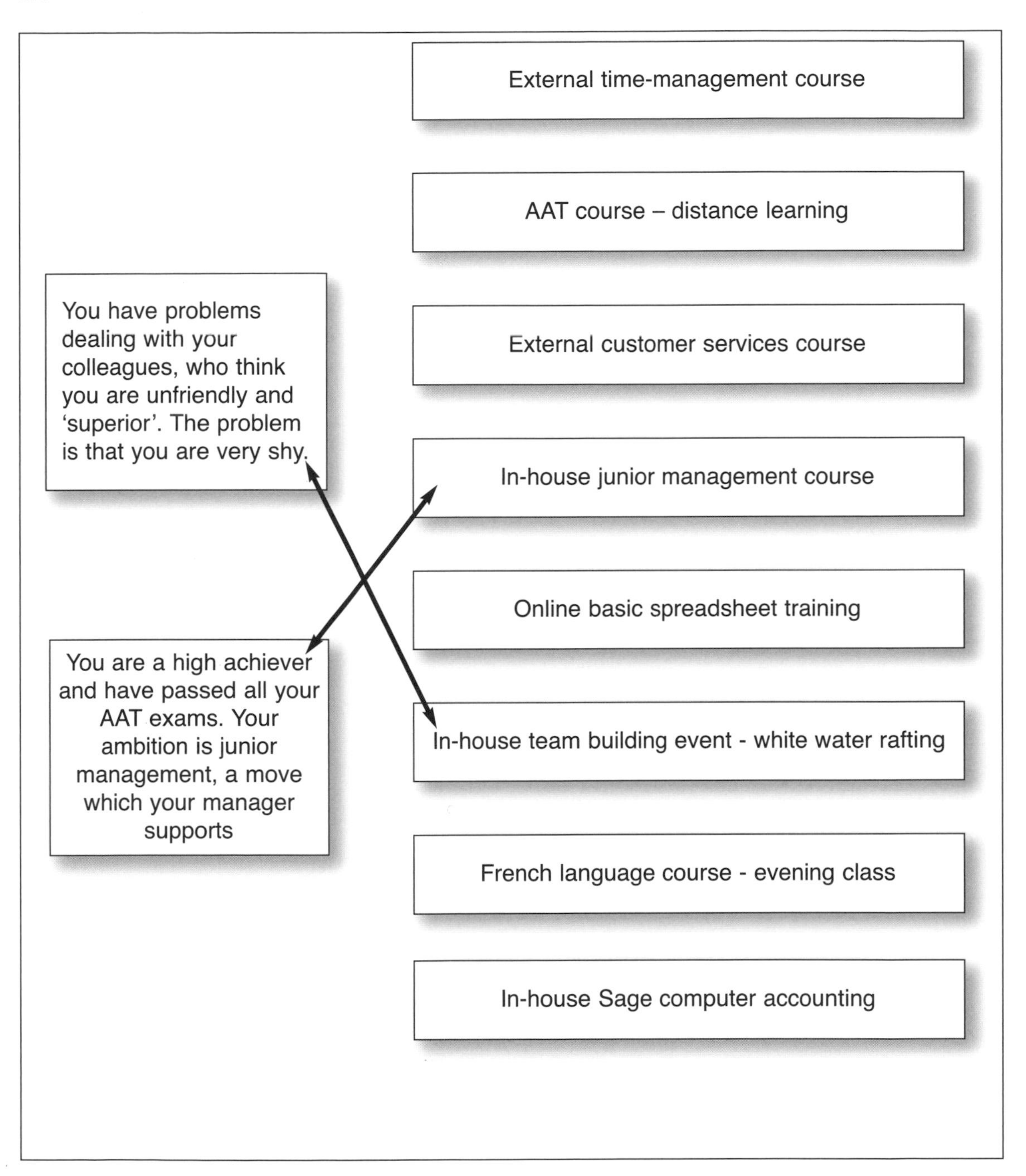
External time-management course
AAT course – distance learning
You have problems dealing with your colleagues, who think you are unfriendly and 'superior'. The problem is that you are very shy.
External customer services course
In-house junior management course
Online basic spreadsheet training
You are a high achiever and have passed all your AAT exams. Your ambition is junior management, a move which your manager supports
In-house team building event - white water rafting
French language course - evening class
In-house Sage computer accounting

Practice assessment 1

Task 1

(a) Which **ONE** of the following policies and procedures is most likely to be relevant to the accounting function? Tick the appropriate option.

	✔
Emergency procedures for fire	
Quality control	
Clothing worn on the production line	
The use of environmentally friendly cleaning materials	

(b) Which **ONE** of the following statements is correct. Tick the appropriate statement.

	✔
Only Line Managers have access to an organisation's policies and procedures	
Using policies and procedures helps employees to work effectively	
Following policies and procedures is essential for obtaining qualifications	
The law requires that there is a set of policies and procedures for payroll	

(c) Which **TWO** of the following are external stakeholders to which a business is likely to provide accounting information? Tick the appropriate options.

	✔
The Production Department	
The tax authorities	
Competitors	
The bank	

Task 2 (a)

The diagram below shows an extract from the organisation chart of a manufacturing business which has four directors and various managers, line managers and assistants.

Complete the empty boxes with the appropriate job roles, using the following job titles:

Finance Director **Managing Director** **Sales Manager** **Production Director**

Sales Ledger Line Manager **Payroll Assistants** **Purchases Ledger Line Manager**

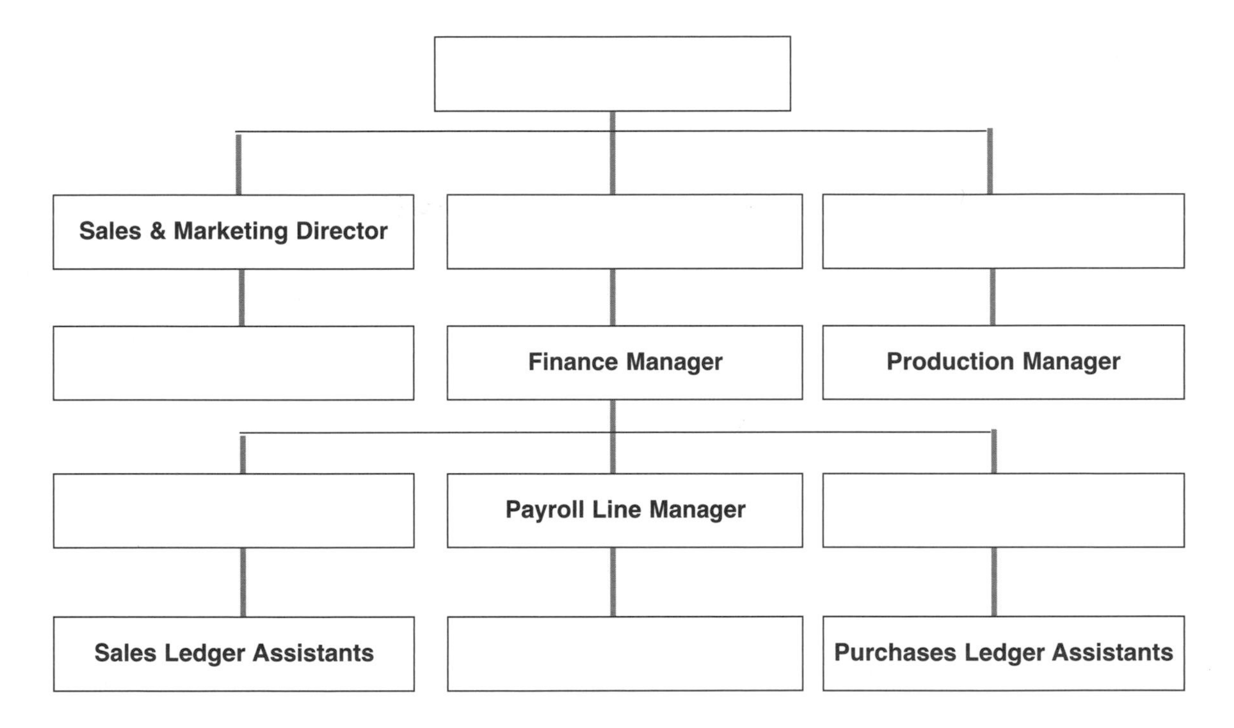

(b) Which **TWO** of the following actions will help to improve the solvency of a business? Tick the appropriate options.

	✔
Paying into the bank once a month	
Giving customers long credit periods	
Giving customers short credit periods	
Paying supplier invoices as soon as they are received	
Sending chaser letters to customers who do not pay on time	
Using cash to pay smaller invoices	

Task 3 (a)

Your name is Lesley Payne (lpayne@iris.co.uk) and you work as an assistant in the Accounts Department of Iris Limited and have been passed the draft email (shown below) to complete.

The email is a request to Mrs Margaret Cameron (mcameron@iris.co.uk), a Line Manager in the Administration Department, to make the arrangements for a presentation of the company's financial results to the Directors and Managers of the company on 20 July. You will need the information by 6 July.

For the presentation you will need:

- a room to seat 40 people
- on 20 July between 11.00 and 12.00
- refreshments (coffee, tea and biscuits) to be served from 10.45
- projection equipment and a support technician
- the cost to be charged to Budget code ACC90871

You are to:

1 Insert the email addresses of the sender and recipient in the appropriate box.

2 Select two appropriate paragraphs from the table set out on the next page. These two paragraphs will need to ensure that all the requirements for the meeting are met. Indicate with a tick your choice of paragraph in the two columns on the right-hand side of the table.

From	
To	
Subject	Presentation of Company financial results

Hello Mrs Cameron

Paragraph 1

Paragraph 2

Many thanks and kind regards

Lesley

Accounts Department

	✔ Paragraph 1	✔ Paragraph 2
We are holding a meeting on 20 June between 11.00 and 12.00 for 40 people and will be grateful if you could arrange a suitable room for us.		
We will need projection equipment and a support technician. We will also need refreshments (coffee, tea and biscuits) to be served from 10.45. All costs are to be charged to Budget code ACC90971. Please can you let me have the details by 6 July.		
We are holding a meeting on 20 July between 11.00 and 12.30 for 40 people and will be grateful if you could arrange a suitable room for us.		
We will need projection equipment and a support technician. We will also need refreshments (coffee, tea and biscuits) to be served from 10.45. All costs are to be charged to Budget code ACC90871. Please can you let me have the details by 6 July.		
We will need projection equipment. We will also need refreshments (coffee, tea and biscuits) to be served from 10.45. All costs are to be charged to Budget code ACC90871. Please can you let me have the details by 6 July.		
The meeting is to be held on 20 July between 11.00 and 12.00 for 60 people and we will be grateful if you could arrange a suitable room for us.		
We are holding a meeting on 20 July between 11.00 and 12.00 for 40 people and will be grateful if you could arrange a suitable room for us.		
We will need projection equipment and a support technician. We will not need refreshments on this occasion. All costs are to be charged to Budget code ACC90871. Please could you let me have all the necessary details by 6 July.		

(b) Indicate below whether the following statements are true or false.

	✔ True	✔ False
All emails are informal and so the punctuation can also be informal		
A 'CC' field on an email means that the email requires a confirmation of receipt		

Task 4

You are an Accounts Assistant employed by Piper Limited. You work in the Sales Ledger section.

Your working hours are 09.00 to 17.00 with an hour for lunch from 13.00 to 14.00.

You have a staff meeting every Tuesday at 11.00 which is compulsory.

Your other duties during the week are set out on the schedule below.

Task description	**Scheduling of tasks**		**Time taken for task**
	Day	**Time**	
Dealing with emails and the post	Daily	9.00	1 hour
Processing sales orders	Daily	10.00	1 hour
Processing payments by customers	Monday	14.00	2 hours
Sales invoicing and credit notes on Sage	Wednesday	14.00	2 hours
Updating the office filing	Thursday	11.00	1 hour
Preparing and sending out customer statements	Thursday	14.00	2 hours
Sending out overdue account letters	Friday	14.00	2 hours

On Wednesday, just as you are about to start to input a large pile of sales invoices on the computer, the main server crashes and all the computers in the office are put out of action. As you cannot input the invoices you carry on with some general filing work and other small jobs that need to be done.

Meanwhile the IT people are called in and the problem is eventually fixed at 4.45 pm.

The Accounts Manager then calls a short meeting for the Accounts Department staff and says:

> *"Sorry about the computer problem. It is all fixed now and you should be fine to carry on as normal tomorrow morning. I don't see the need to work any overtime now as I am sure you can catch up with your work then.*
>
> *Please make sure that you carry out your normal routines as usual, in other words tasks like opening the post, answering emails and order processing; these need to be done and got out of the way first.*
>
> *Lastly, this week is the last week of the month. It is critical that all the customer invoices and credit notes are input and printed, and the ledgers updated. We can then produce statements as usual tomorrow afternoon and send out overdue account letters on Friday."*

(a) Write a 'to do' list for Thursday by listing the tasks in order of completion in the table set out below. Write the task descriptions in the column on the right.

Choose from the following tasks:

Dealing with emails and the post

Processing payments by customers

Processing sales orders

Sending out overdue account letters

Updating the office filing

Preparing and sending out customer statements

Sales invoicing and credit notes on Sage

THURSDAY 'TO DO' LIST (in order of completion)	
Task 1	
Task 2	
Task 3	
Task 4	
Task 5	

(b) If you **do not carry out the instructions** of the Accounts Manager there could be problems. Tick the **THREE** likely outcomes that would occur if you **did not** reorganise your priority of tasks.

	✔
If statements or chaser letters are sent out late this would adversely affect the cash flow of the business	
Processing of payments received from customers would be delayed	
The overdue account letters might not be produced on time	
The office filing might be delayed	
The post may not get opened	
The statements might not be produced on time	

Task 5

You work in the Sales Ledger Section of the Accounts Department of Fanway Fertilisers. You have recently been reviewing the various customer accounts and your Manager has agreed to increase the trade discount and payment terms allowed to Topsham Topiary Ltd.

The current arrangements are for a 30% trade discount and 30 days credit but the decision is to increase this to 35% and 60 days. The reason for this is that Topsham Topiary (an important customer) may be looking to take its business elsewhere if the trading terms are not improved.

An appropriate letter is to be sent to Mrs B Box, Sales Director of Topsham Topiary Ltd.

The Sales Ledger account code for this customer is TOP24628.

The draft of the letter to be sent to Topsham Topiary Ltd is shown below. **You are to:**

(a) Review the letter carefully and identify **eight** words (including collections of letters and numbers) which are either **spelt** incorrectly or **used** incorrectly. Enter them in the left-hand column of the table below.

(b) Enter your correction of these eight words on the appropriate line in the right-hand column of the table below.

> Dear Mr Box
>
> Trading terms: Account Topsham Topiary Ltd, ref. TOP244628
>
> We have recently been reviewing your account and are delighted to advise that we are able to ammend your terms of trading as follows: trade discount will be inceased from 30% to 35% and the payment period will be increased from 30 days to 60 days.
>
> This will take affect from 1 June. If their are any queries that you might have, please do not hesitate to get in touch with me.
>
> Your's faithfully

incorrect word	correction

Task 6

Jem Trading Limited is a UK company which divides its sales force into four regions. The provisional sales figures for the last three months are shown below.

Region	**Sales (£)** **January - March**
South	456,400
West	349,340
North	410,520
East	274,840

You have been asked to do some analysis of these figures and to carry out the tasks that follow.

(a) What are the total UK sales for January to March? £

(b) What percentage of total sales was made by the North Region? Round your answer to two decimal places. %

(c) What percentage of total sales was made by the South Region and the West Region combined? Round your answer to two decimal places. %

(d) The Sales Manager estimates that the total UK sales for the next three months will increase by $^1/_5$ over the January-March figure. What is the amount of this increase? £

(e) What is the total estimated UK sales figure for April to June? £

(f) Based on the estimate in (e) what is the percentage increase in UK Sales from January-March to April-June? Express your answer as a whole number. %

Your manager then tells you that there is a mistake in the way the January-March figures have been compiled and says that £100,000 of sales have been allocated to the South Region which should have been allocated to the East Region.

(g) Calculate the revised sales figures in the table below by adjusting the sales figures for the South Region and the East Region by the amount of the error.

(h) Enter the total of the four Regions' sales in the total box.

Region	**Revised Sales (£)** **January - March**
South	
West	
North	
East	
Total sales	

(i) What is the **revised** percentage of total sales made by the South Region? Round your answer to two decimal places.

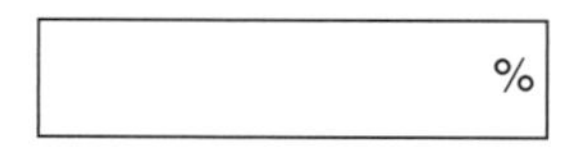

(j) What is the **revised** percentage of total sales made by the East Region? Round your answer to two decimal places.

%

Task 7

You are an Accounts Assistant in a large holiday travel company. You have recently had a staff appraisal and your manager has reviewed your performance and helped you identify your strengths and weaknesses.

Your manager has discussed with you a number of ways in which you can improve your performance (remedying weaknesses) and also develop your skills (developing your strengths).

The two areas for development are:

1 **Customer services skills**
You have problems dealing with customers. You sometimes lose your cool, get confused and make mistakes.

2 **Computerised accounting**
You do well in your computer work and want to move into working on computerised accounting programs for payroll and invoicing.

You are to:

(a) Select the **TWO** most appropriate development activities from the list in the table below – ie **one for each** of the two development needs.

Indicate in the second column the number 1 or 2 to show which development need the chosen activity is appropriate to (customer services = 1, computerised accounting = 2)

Enter in the far right column the likely timescale for completion of the activity. By 'timescale' it means 'when would it be best for you to complete the training?' Sooner or later? Possible completion timescales are within 3 months, 12 months, or 24 months.

Development activity	1 or 2?	Completion (months)
External time-management course (8 week)		
AAT Level 2 Certificate course – by distance learning		
External customer services 6 week short course		
In-house junior 8 weeks management course		
Short-course (10 week) basic spreadsheet training		
In-house one day team building event - white water rafting		
French language course - evening class (10 months)		
In-house 6 month Sage computer accounting training		

(b) Objectives for personal development set in the CPD process are said to be 'SMART', which stands for:

Specific

Measurable

Achievable

Realistic

Time bound

Each of the following five numbered sentences describes one of the five types of objective.

Enter the appropriate sentence number in the table which follows against the type of objective that it describes.

1 The objective should be within the capabilities of the employee.

2 The objective should be capable of being achieved within a certain period of time.

3 The employee should be able and willing to achieve the objective.

4 The objective should be clear and well-defined.

5 The employee and manager should be able to tell how successfully the objective is being achieved.

SMART objective	**Sentence number**
Specific	
Measurable	
Achievable	
Realistic	
Time bound	

Task 8

(a) A business report normally contains seven sections, each with a distinct function. The seven sections are:

1 Title
2 Summary
3 Introduction
4 Findings
5 Conclusions
6 Recommendations
7 Appendices

You are to match the two sections on the left with the appropriate descriptions on the right. Draw two lines as appropriate.

Section title	Section contents
	A short explanation (often for managers and executives) summarising the areas the report examines.
	This sets out and analyses the results of the investigations of the report.
Conclusions	A single page stating what the report is about, who wrote it, and the date it was written.
	This sets out the information gathered by the report and is the basis for the conclusions.
Introduction	The suggested course(s) of action which are based on the report.
	Additional information which supports the report but is not contained in the Findings.
	This section tells the reader how the report came about and explains the nature of the tasks and the people involved.

Task 8 (continued)

Padella Limited is an old-fashioned manufacturing company. Many of its accounting systems are manual, although it has recently set up a computerised system which operates the ledgers. The Accounts Manager has been asked to produce a Report based on the investigation of the current payroll system which is totally paper-based and expensive to operate. Her main task is to reduce costs in the business.

You are a Costing Assistant and have been asked to investigate the annual costs of **three options** and see how they work out over a three year period, and decide which is the least expensive.

Option 1 the existing manual system as it stands, which is very labour-intensive

Option 2 the possibility of computerising the system, which will need updated computer equipment and require staff training

Option 3 paying an external payroll bureau to process the payroll

Your findings, which will be incorporated in the Report, are as follows:

	Annual running cost (£)	**Set-up costs (£)**
Manual payroll system (in-house)	4,000	None
Computerised payroll (in-house)	1,200	7,500
Payroll bureau (external)	5,000	None

You have also calculated:

1 the **total cost for 3 years** (ie annual costs plus any set-up costs) for each option

2 the **average cost per year** of each option (ie total cost divided by 3)

These results have been set out in the following table:

PADELLA LIMITED – 3 YEAR PAYROLL COST AND AVERAGE COST PER YEAR				
Payroll system used	**Total annual running cost (3 x annual running cost)** £	**Set-up cost** £	**Total cost for 3 years** £	**Average annual cost** £
Manual payroll (in-house)	4,000 x 3 = 12,000	0	12,000	4,000
Computerised payroll (in-house)	1,200 x 3 = 3,600	7,500	11,100	3,700
Payroll bureau (external)	5,000 x 3 = 15,000	0	15,000	5,000

Now complete the two tasks which follow.

(b) Select **TWO conclusions** to be included in the Report. The conclusions should be based on the **cost** of the three options calculated on the previous page. Tick the appropriate boxes.

	✔
The existing manual payroll system is the cheapest option over the three years	
The computerised payroll system is the cheapest option over the three years	
It would be better and cheaper in the long run to have the payroll processed by an external payroll bureau	
It would not be a good idea to use the computerised payroll option because the set-up costs are so high	
It would be a good idea to use the computerised payroll option because the set-up costs are only a 'one-off' expense and the long-term total costs are lower	
It would be a good idea to use the external payroll bureau because it would reduce the need for staff training	

(c) Select **TWO recommendations** to be included in the Report and based on the conclusions in (b) above. Tick the appropriate boxes.

	✔
Call a meeting of Accounts staff who work on payroll and tell them that they will be expected to work more efficiently when using the manual system	
Call a meeting of Accounts staff and explain to them the benefits using a computerised accounting system and promise them suitable training	
Call a staff meeting and tell the employees that the payroll will be processed by an external bureau	
Draw up a plan for the extra computer equipment that will be needed and obtain further information about computer accounting training courses	

Task 9

(a) The objectives of an effective team will be to (indicate the correct option):

	✔
Work to a high standard, quickly, delegating tasks where possible	
Work to a high standard, within deadlines, and efficiently	
Work within deadlines, efficiently and letting the manager prioritise tasks	

(b) You work as an assistant in a Payroll Section of an Accounts Department. A new assistant who has recently been transferred from another section has been given a desk next to you. He spends a lot of time looking at the Procedures Manual and not completing his work on time, and when he does complete it he sometimes makes mistakes. You do not have time to help him. The situation is causing a lot of dissatisfaction in the Payroll Section and nobody is doing anything about it.

(1) What effect could this behaviour have? Select the appropriate option.

	✔
No effect because the Department has just finished its payroll run	
It could reflect badly on you because you are not helping him	
It could reflect badly on the Department and also the organisation because the payroll could get delayed and employees might receive the incorrect pay	

(2) What steps could you take to resolve the problem? Select the appropriate option.

	✔
Do nothing at all because you would like him to get a transfer elsewhere	
Mention the problem to your Line Manager if the situation does not improve	
Mention the problem to the Human Resources Manager	

Task 10

(a) Tick the **TWO** of the following which **are** fundamental principles of ethics in the workplace.

	✔
Effectiveness	
Efficiency	
Integrity	
Motivation	
Equality	

(b) Identify and tick the **TWO** examples below of a breach of confidentiality in an Accounting Department.

	✔
A local firm of accountants has been appointed by your company to undertake the annual audit of your company's accounts. They are on your premises and they are given the payroll details of all the company's employees	
A customer calls and asks you for the telephone number of one of your colleagues, as it is an emergency. You give the customer the number	
You are moved to the payroll section and notice that all the salary slips of the staff are being printed out and you can see how much the Accounts Manager earns. You mention this amount to a colleague	
Your partner works in the same office as you and you discuss one of your customers over the breakfast table. Nobody else is present	

(c) A 'conflict of interest' is associated with which **ONE** of the following fundamental principles of ethics in the workplace.

	✔
Professional behaviour	
Objectivity	
Professional competence and due care	

Task 11

(a) Identify which **FOUR** of the following are examples of a sustainability policy within an organisation.

	✔
Sponsorship of a local school sports event	
Using suppliers who charge the lowest prices	
Using the cheapest paper in the photocopiers	
Financing an employee to take an AAT qualification	
Using suppliers who source their products from overseas	
Organising 'cycle to work' schemes	
Asking staff to turn out the lights at the end of the working day	
Setting product prices high to improve profitability	

(b) Which **ONE** of the following is the most accurate description of the meaning of 'Corporate Social Responsibility'? Tick the appropriate option.

	✔
The need for a company to support socialist political principles	
The need for a company to adopt a strategy for promoting sustainable principles	
A company's responsibility to provide training courses for staff which encourage staff to 'bond' and work effectively together	

Practice assessment 2

Task 1

(a) The policies and procedures to be followed by an Accounting Department of an organisation are (choose **ONE** option):

	✔
Established by the main UK professional accounting bodies	
Established by the Human Resources Department of the organisation	
Set up by the organisation itself	
Set out in Health and Safety law	

(b) Which **TWO** of the following policies and procedures are most likely to be relevant to the accounting function?

	✔
Grievance procedures for staff complaints	
Environmental policy	
Quality control in manufacture	
Emergency procedures for suspected letter bomb	

(c) A stakeholder of a business is likely to be interested in accounting information. Match the stakeholder in the left-hand column with the most appropriate accounting information in the right-hand column. Draw lines linking the stakeholders to the types of information.

Stakeholder
HM Revenue & Customs
Bank
Suppliers

Accounting information
Cash available to repay loans
Checking supplier invoices
VAT figures
Credit record for payment of trade debts
Payroll calculations
Petty cash book

Task 2

(a) The diagram below shows an extract from the organisation chart of a services business which has three directors and various managers, line managers and assistants.

Complete the empty boxes with the appropriate job roles, using the following job titles:

Marketing Director **Human Resources Manager** **Payroll Line Manager**

Costing Assistant **Sales Ledger Line Manager** **Managing Director**

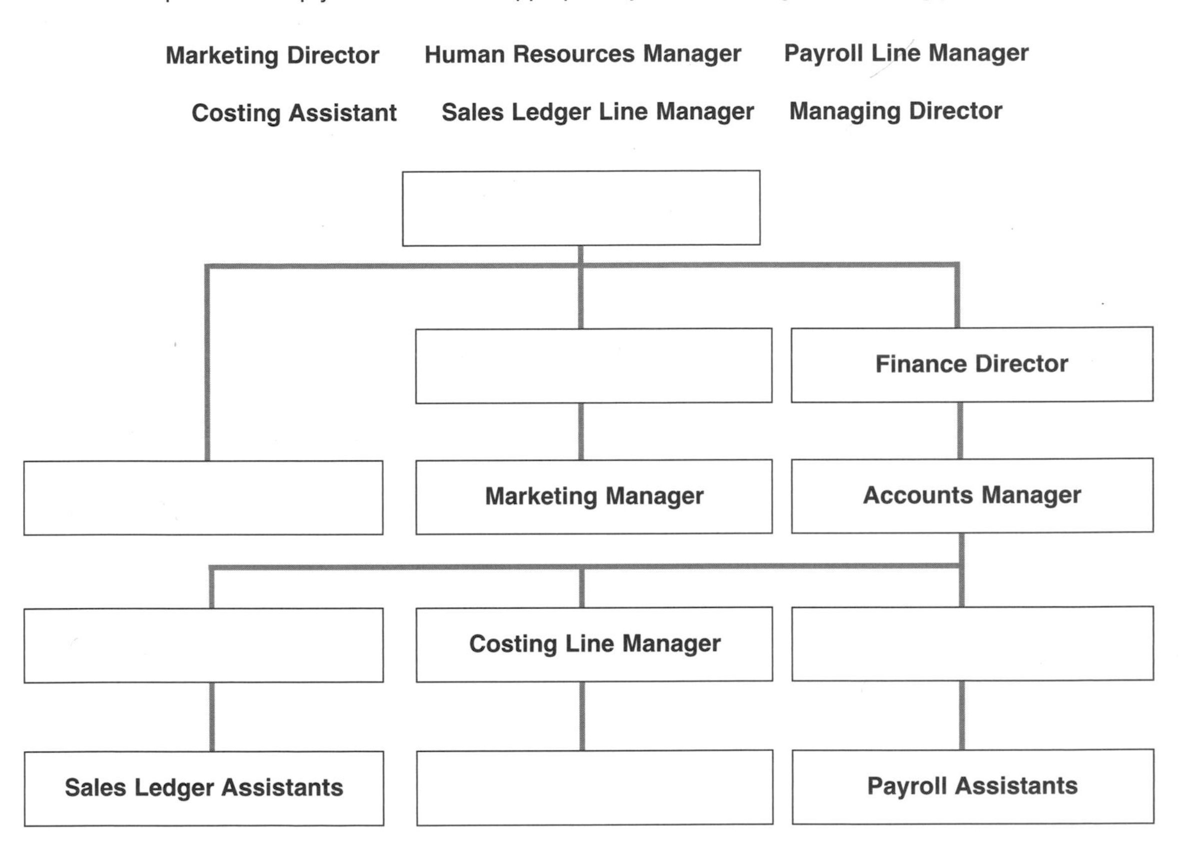

(b) A Line Manager in charge of the Purchases Ledger section of an Accounting Department is likely to be reported to by (indicate the correct option):

	✔
Purchases Ledger Assistants only	
Assistants in the Accounting Department only	
Assistants from a variety of Departments	

(c) Indicate with a tick in the table below whether the actions described **will** or **will not** help the solvency of an organisation.

action	**will help solvency** ✔	**will not help solvency** ✔
Paying into the bank frequently		
Giving customers short credit periods		
Paying into the bank once a month to save petrol		
Paying supplier invoices later rather than sooner		
Using company credit cards for staff expenses		
Giving customers long credit periods		

Task 3

(a) Your name is Gina Ciambella (gciambella@archo.co.uk) and you work as an assistant in the Payroll Section of the Accounts Department of Archo Limited and have been passed the draft email (shown below) to complete.

The email is a request to Jo Green (jgreen@archo.co.uk), an assistant in the Human Resources Department, to provide details of hours worked in March by all the employees of the company, listed by Department. You need the information by 5 April.

You are to:

(1) Insert the email address of the recipient in the appropriate box.

(2) Complete the remaining boxes (they are numbered for reference) with the most appropriate words or phrases from the lists shown below (also numbered for reference).

From gciambella@archo.co.uk

To [ ]

Subject [1]

Hi Jo

Please send me the hours worked by [2]

for the month of [3]. It would be useful if you could send

me this data on the usual spreadsheet. I need the information by [4].

Many thanks and kind regards

Gina

Payroll Section, Accounts Department

Option Lists

Pick the most suitable word or phrase for each numbered box from the following numbered lists:

1 Payroll, Hours, March payroll data, March

2 employees in the Accounts Department, all employees by Department, the Department

3 March, April, May, June

4 5 March, 15 March, 5 April, 15 April

(b) Indicate below whether the following statements are true or false.

	✔ True	✔ False
It is normal practice when writing emails to write ALL URGENT REQUESTS IN CAPITAL LETTERS		
It is normal practice when writing emails to copy in all members of your own Department		

Task 4

You are an Accounts Assistant employed by Miller Limited. You carry out a wide variety of tasks.

Your working hours are 09.00 to 17.00 with an hour for lunch from 13.00 to 14.00. Staff do not normally work overtime as a matter of policy, except if the situation is absolutely critical.

You have a staff meeting every Friday at 11.00 which is compulsory.

Your other duties during the week are set out on the schedule below.

Task description	**Scheduling of tasks**		**Time taken for task**
	Day	**Time**	
Dealing with emails and the post	Daily	9.00	1 hour
Processing sales invoices	Daily	10.00	1 hour
Processing payments to suppliers	Tuesday	11.00	2 hours
Credit control - sending chasers	Wednesday	15.00	2 hours
Processing the payroll	Thursday	15.00	2 hours
Listing the cheques and cash for paying in at the bank	Friday	12.00	1 hour
Paying in at the bank	Friday	14.00	1 hour

One Thursday afternoon just as you are leaving the office you receive the following email from the Accounts Manager:

> Hi Alex
>
> I am having a meeting here at 12.00 tomorrow with John Lucas, Finance Director of Gerda Construction Ltd.
>
> Can you let me have all the latest sales figures, credit limit and account history on my desk by 11.00 on Friday latest, please.
>
> Sorry about the short notice.
>
> Thanks

(a) The Manager's request will obviously put you under pressure, but you should be able to do the job if you prioritise your tasks carefully. Consider the ways in which you should deal with the Manager's request for the figures for Friday's meeting and tick the option below which you think is the most appropriate.

	✔
Email to say that your work schedule will not allow you to do the task in time	
Reply to say that you will have the figures for him if you can do overtime on Thursday evening	
Confirm that you will have the figures for him in time for his meeting on Friday	
Do not reply to him but just hope that you can provide the figures in time	

(b) Complete the 'to do' list for Friday set out below by listing the tasks in order of completion. Write the task descriptions in the column on the right.

Choose from the following tasks:

Dealing with emails and the post

Processing sales invoices

Processing payments to suppliers

Credit control - sending chasers

Processing the payroll

Listing the cheques and cash for paying in at the bank

Paying in at the bank

Preparing account information for Gerda Construction Ltd

FRIDAY 'TO DO' LIST (in order of completion)	
Task 1	
Task 2	
Task 3	
Task 4	
Task 5	

Task 5

You work in the Purchases Ledger Section of the Accounts Department of Fancy Farm Foods. You have received a query from a supplier, Dairy Delights Ltd. They have not received a payment for £12,957.50 sent by your company by Faster Payment bank transfer on 22 March.

You check the bank account online and see that a payment for that amount left the bank account on 22 March. You ask the bank to check the payment and they report that because of a system shutdown on that day, the amount was not sent. They stated that it would be sent straightaway.

An appropriate letter is to be sent to Mrs C Reeme, Sales Manager of Dairy Delights Ltd. The account code for Fancy Farm Foods used by the supplier is FF28742.

The draft of the letter to be sent to Dairy Delights Ltd is shown below.

You are to:

(a) Review the letter carefully and identify **eight** words (including collections of letters and numbers) which are either **spelt** incorrectly or **used** incorrectly. Enter them in the left-hand column of the table below.

(b) Enter your correction of these eight words on the appropriate line in the right-hand column of the table below.

> Dear Miss Reeme
>
> Account Fancy Farm Foods, ref. FF287442, Payment for £12,957.00
>
> We would like to appologise for the fact that you have not recieved our payment for 12,957.50 what we sent on 22 March.
>
> We have checked this matter with our bank and they have adviced us that it was not sent because they experienced a major system shutdown on that day. They will be sending the amount to your bank account today.
>
> Your sincerely

incorrect word	correction

Task 6

Mazota is a Korean car manufacturer which has a factory in Milton Keynes. It produces four models:

- the Whizz, a 2 wheel drive town car
- the Fourlander, a 4 wheel drive car
- the Sportstar, a 2 wheel drive sports car
- the Rugged, a 4 wheel drive car

Workers on each of the production lines compete to be as efficient as possible. The workers on the production line that produces the most cars receive a productivity pay bonus of 10% every three months. The amount paid is based on the average monthly pay of production workers.

The number of cars produced in the three month period of April to June and the average number of workers on each production line was as follows:

Vehicle	Cars produced April - June	Production line workers
Whizz	15,500	250
Fourlander (4 wheel drive)	23,250	310
Sportstar	31,000	450
Rugged (4 wheel drive)	7,750	190

You have been asked to do some analysis of these figures and to carry out the tasks that follow.

(a) What is the total number of cars produced from April to June?

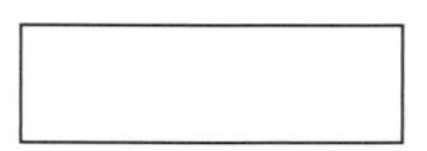

(b) What percentage of total cars produced was made on the Whizz production line? Round your answer to the nearest whole figure.

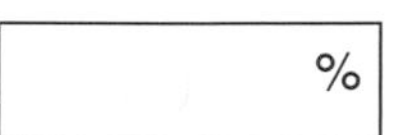

(c) What percentage of total cars produced was made on the two 4 wheel drive cars production lines? Add the two production line figures together. Round your answer to the nearest whole figure.

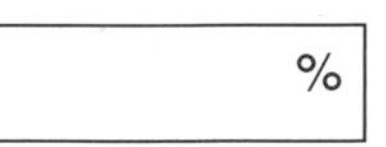

(d) What fraction of total car production was produced on the Whizz production line?

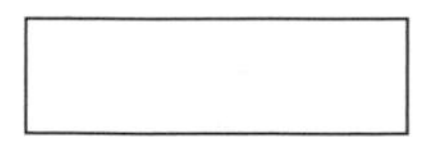

(e) The average monthly pay of the Mazota production workers is £2,100. The workers that received the productivity bonus in June of 10% would receive in total in June (tick the correct amount):

	✔
£2,100 each	
£2,310 each	
£4,200 each	

(f) The average number of cars produced on the four production lines for the period from April to June was which of the following? (Use the formula: total number of cars produced divided by the number of production lines.)

	✔
19,375	
23,250	
31,000	

(g) The total number of production line workers in the factory is

(h) The total monthly wage bill for all production workers before any productivity bonuses and based on the figures given is:

£

(i) The total monthly wage bill for all production workers before any productivity bonuses, written in words is:

	✔
Twenty five million and twenty thousand pounds	
Two million, five hundred and twenty thousand pounds	
Twenty five thousand two hundred pounds	

Task 7

Your manager has recently reviewed your performance and identified your strengths and weaknesses. She has suggested a number of ways in which you can improve your performance (remedying weaknesses) and develop your skills (developing your strengths).

The two areas which need special attention are :

Area 1 **Spreadsheets**
You have problems with handling spreadsheets and wish to gain confidence and skills in this area.

Area 2 **Accounting Qualifications**
You are keen to progress and would like to take accounting exams. You are a mother of two young children and cannot get to college. You would like to try the introductory level of learning first and the see how you get on.

You are to:

(a) Select the **TWO** most appropriate development activities from the list in the table below – ie **one for each** of the two development needs.

Indicate in the second column the number 1 or 2 to show which development need the chosen activity is appropriate to (Area 1 = Spreadsheets, Area 2 = Accounting Qualifications).

Enter in the far right column the likely timescale for completion of the activity. By 'timescale' it means 'when would it be best for you to complete the training?' Sooner or later? Possible completion timescales are within 3 months, 12 months, or 24 months.

Development activity	1 or 2?	Completion (months)
External time-management course (8 week)		
AAT Level 2 Certificate course – by distance learning		
External customer services 6 week short course		
In-house junior 8 weeks management course		
Short-course (10 week) basic spreadsheet training		
In-house one-day team building event - white water rafting		
French language course - evening class (10 months)		
In-house 6 month Sage computer accounting training		

(b) Continuing Professional Development involves four separate processes which take place in a specific order.

The four processes (not necessarily in the correct order) are:

What are my objectives?

What are my development needs now?

How well have I achieved them?

How can I achieve my objectives?

You are to complete the following table with the four processes in the order in which they should take place.

Task 8

You work in the Accounts Department of the Leeds office of DirectInsure, a national insurance broking business.

Your office, which is modern and open-plan, has been selected for an experimental trial in layout and organisation along the lines of 'hot desking'. This means that each employee does not have an individual desk but has to go wherever there is a spare desk available.

Each desk has a computer linked to the central server. The consequence of this arrangement is that each employee has to carry around in a trolley all the necessary stationery and paperwork.

DirectInsure is worried that this will 'depersonalise' the office as employees will not be allowed to personalise their work space with the usual collection of photos, plants, and other personal items.

The management will review the success or otherwise of this experiment after a six month period and write a report. If the scheme is a success it will be adopted in other DirectInsure offices.

A questionnaire is circulated to the 40 staff at the end of the six months. The questionnaire and the results are shown below. These will be incorporated in the report.

QUESTION	RESPONSE		
	yes	**no**	**neither yes nor no**
The briefing for the new system was helpful.	33	2	5
The opinions of the staff were respected.	23	7	10
The system works efficiently and you always got a desk when you wanted it.	22	14	4
The working environment was improved and you worked more effectively.	12	24	4
You missed the personalised desk area that you were used to.	26	6	8
You would recommend that other DirectInsure offices would benefit from the change to hot desking.	12	18	10

The Accounts Manager and her Line Managers have a meeting to discuss these results and also some other statistics:

- absenteeism from the Department has increased by 10% over the six months
- the management has received 15% more complaints than usual about working practices and office procedures
- more complaints than usual have been received from customers about the levels of customer service, eg a longer response time to queries, a decrease in staff friendliness

(a) You are to identify from the statements below **THREE** conclusions and **TWO** recommendations that you would suggest to the management that they include in their report. These will be based on the findings shown on the previous page and will provide an accurate view of what the trial-run has revealed about the way 'hot desking' works in practice.

When you have made your choice, tick the appropriate column on the right.

	conclusion ✔	recommendation ✔
The briefing for the trial-run was not very helpful and the opinions of the staff were not respected.		
Hot desking should be discontinued in the Accounts Department.		
The working environment was not improved and this led to less effective working by the Department.		
Hot desking should be introduced in the other DirectInsure offices.		
It was beneficial not to have desks cluttered up with personal possessions.		
Staff missed being able to personalise their desks with their belongings.		
Hot desking should not be introduced in the other DirectInsure offices.		
Hot desking had a bad effect on the levels of customer service provided.		
Staff were motivated by the new system, absenteeism was reduced and fewer complaints received.		
Hot desking should be continued in the Accounts Department.		

(b) In which section of the report should the individual responses to the questionnaire be included? Tick the correct option.

	✔
Introduction	
Executive summary	
Appendices	
Main body	

Task 9

(a) Dissatisfaction within a team requires action. If nothing is done about the problem, the effectiveness of the team could be affected.

Sometimes it is up to a team member to take action, in other situations the matter should be reported to a higher authority, a Line Manager, for example.

Assume that you are an Accounts Assistant and indicate below which issues can be resolved by you, and which will need to be referred to a Line Manager.

	✔ **by you**	✔ **by a manager**
A colleague keeps taking your crisps		
A colleague keeps taking office postage stamps		
A colleague has bad body odour		

(b) On Thursday morning your Line Manager asks you to make sure that you complete by 2.00pm the credit slips for paying in at the bank that afternoon. This is earlier than normal because money is normally paid in on a Friday. This is a problem because the Senior Accounts Manager has asked you for the top 20 customer sales figures by Thursday lunchtime as he has a credit control meeting at 2.00pm. You will not have time to complete both tasks.

Select the most appropriate action from the following options.

	✔
Carry out the sales figures task for the Senior Accounts Manager, as she is more important, and paying in at the bank could always wait until another day.	
Complete the credit slips for the bank and the sales figures as quickly as you can, leaving out the normal checking processes, hoping that you will be able to carry out both tasks within the set deadlines.	
Discuss your workload with your Line Manager and explain that you cannot carry out both tasks within the set deadlines. He can then decide how to allocate the tasks to his staff so that both deadlines are met.	

(c) Identify from the list below **TWO** characteristics of an effective accounts team.

	✔
Members can rely on other members to complete the work on time	
Members will support colleagues and provide help when required	
Members complete tasks within given deadlines	
Members will always be able to deal with dissatisfaction without having to refer to a higher authority	

Task 10

(a) Tick the **TWO** of the following which **are** fundamental principles of ethics in the workplace.

	✔
Professional behaviour	
Professional competence and due care	
Professional responsibility	
Integrality	
Inequality	

(b) Identify and tick the **TWO** examples below of a breach of confidentiality in an accounting department.

	✔
A local firm of accountants has been appointed by your company to undertake the annual audit of your company's accounts. They are on your premises and they are given the payroll details of all the company's employees.	
A customer calls and asks you for the telephone number of one of your colleagues, as it is an emergency. You give the customer the number.	
You are moved to the payroll section and notice that all the salary slips of the staff are being printed out and you can see how much the Accounts Manager earns. You mention this amount to a colleague.	
Your partner works in the same office as you and you discuss one of your customers at home over the breakfast table. Nobody else is present.	

(c) A 'conflict of interest' is associated with which **ONE** of the following fundamental principles of ethics in the workplace.

	✔
Professional behaviour	
Objectivity	
Professional competence and due care	

Task 11

(a) Identify which **FOUR** of the following are examples of a sustainability policy within an organisation.

	✔
Ensuring health and safety in the workplace	
Taking students from local schools on work experience schemes	
Avoiding conflicts of interest in the workplace	
Using suppliers who source their products from renewable resources	
Asking staff to turn off the computers at the end of the working day	
Improving sales to increase profitability	
Organising 'car-sharing' schemes for employees coming to work	
Installing low cost photocopiers	

(b) A policy of sustainability in the workplace can sometimes provide financial benefits to an organisation. Indicate in the table below the **TWO** policies which will help to increase profitability.

	✔
Efficient use of materials, eg using both sides of paper for printing documents	
The use of low energy light bulbs	
The use of expensive packaging which is made from recycled cardboard	

Practice assessment 3

Task 1

(a) Which **ONE** of the following is **not** normally covered by the Policies and Procedures Manual of an Accounting Department?

	✔
Authorisation limits for the signing of cheques	
Authorisation limits for ordering goods and services	
Setting the tax codes issued for calculating employees' pay	
Operation of the petty cash system	

(b) Which **TWO** of the following policies and procedures are likely to affect the accounting function of an organisation?

	✔
Staff disciplinary measures	
Dress code for sales staff	
Use of the company logo in advertising material	
Emergency procedures for a fire alarm	

(c) Which **TWO** of the following stakeholders is an Accounts Assistant most likely to communicate with on a frequent basis?

	✔
Shareholders	
The local community	
Suppliers	
Government Departments	
Banks	

Task 2

(a) The person in an Accounts Department most likely to report to the Managing Director is:

	✔
Finance Director	
Sales Director	
Costing Assistant	
Payroll Manager	

(b) The person in an Accounts Department most directly responsible for a Sales Ledger Assistant is:

	✔
Sales Manager	
Purchases Ledger Line Manager	
Payroll Line Manager	
Sales Ledger Line Manager	

(c) Solvency can be achieved by careful management of money coming in and out of an organisation. State whether or not the following actions help improve solvency. Tick the appropriate box.

	yes ✔	no ✔
Offering settlement discount to your customers		
Keeping a schedule of when your customer accounts need to be paid		
Giving longer credit periods to customers to encourage sales		
Investing surplus cash in a bank account which offers a high rate of interest but requires twelve months notice of withdrawal		

Task 3 (a)

Your name is Peter Grimes and you are the Accounts Department Manager at Suffolk Fisheries. You are in the processing of drafting an email (shown below).

The email is a request to James Finn (jamesfinn@suffolkfisheries.co.uk), Assistant in the Sales and Marketing Department, to update and send the spreadsheet which shows the monthly comparative sales of different types of fish for this and last year. You need the figures urgently, by the end of the day.

You are to:

(1) Insert the email address of the recipient in the appropriate box.

(2) Complete the remaining boxes (they are numbered for reference) with the most appropriate and correctly spelt words or phrases from the lists shown below (also numbered for reference).

From petergrimes@suffolkfisheries.co.uk

To [ ]

Subject Comparative sales figures (all products)

[1]

Please send me [2] the latest sales spreadsheet which shows the [3] comparative figures for all products. I need these figures [4].

[5]

Peter Grimes, Manager, Accounts Department

Option Lists

Pick the most suitable word or phrase for each numbered box from the following numbered lists:

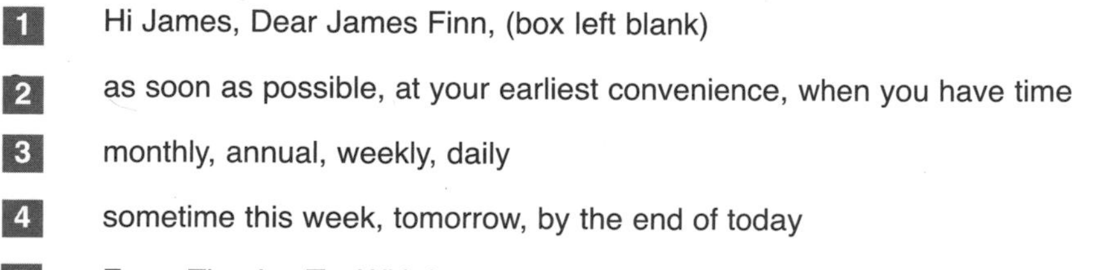

1 Hi James, Dear James Finn, (box left blank)

2 as soon as possible, at your earliest convenience, when you have time

3 monthly, annual, weekly, daily

4 sometime this week, tomorrow, by the end of today

5 Fanx, Thanks, Ta, With immense gratitude

(b) Indicate below whether the following statements are true or false.

	True ✔	False ✔
The language used in an email should always be informal		
When writing emails it is not a good idea to use a lot of 'smileys', ie punctuation or symbols used to show a smiley face (or a sad face)		

Task 4

You are an Accounts Assistant employed by Hockney Limited and work on the Purchases Ledger Section.

Your working hours are 09.00 to 17.00 with an hour for lunch from 13.00 to 14.00.

You have a staff meeting every Monday at 11.00 which is compulsory.

Your other duties during the week are set out on the schedule below.

Task description	Scheduling of tasks		Time taken for task
	Day	Time	
Dealing with emails and the post	Daily	9.00	1 hour
Processing purchase orders	Daily	10.00	1 hour
Processing returns to suppliers	Tuesday	11.00	2 hours
Inventory count	Wednesday	14.00	3 hours
Processing invoices from suppliers	Thursday	15.00	2 hours
Preparing cheque and BACS payments to suppliers	Friday	12.00	1 hour
Working at office of subsidiary company	Friday	14.00	3 hours

On Wednesday morning just before lunch you receive the following email from the Accounts Manager:

> Hi Charlie
>
> As you know I am currently carrying out the six-monthly staff appraisal interviews, but have been called away unexpectedly next week when your interview was scheduled.
>
> Please can you come and see me at 2.00pm tomorrow (Thursday) afternoon instead.
>
> Please let me know if there is any problem.
>
> Thanks

(a) As you are very busy at the moment, particularly in the middle of the week, this will need some time planning, but you should be able to do it if you prioritise your tasks. Tick the option below which seems to you the best solution in the circumstances.

	✔
Ask your Union representative if this is acceptable practice	
Email the Manager to ask if the appraisal could take place in a week or two when you are less busy	
Do not reply to the email because you think it is an unreasonable request	
Email the Manager to say that you will be able to attend the appraisal	

(b) Write a 'to do' list for Wednesday afternoon/Thursday set out below by listing the tasks in order of completion. Write the task descriptions in the column on the right.

Choose from the following tasks:

Dealing with emails and the post

Processing purchase orders

Processing returns to suppliers

Inventory count

Processing invoices from suppliers

Preparing cheque and BACS payments to suppliers

Working at the office of subsidiary company

Attending the appraisal interview

WEDNESDAY AFTERNOON/THURSDAY 'TO DO' LIST (in order of completion)	
Task 1	
Task 2	
Task 3	
Task 4	
Task 5	

Task 5

You have been passed the following draft letter on 1 April for checking. It is being sent to a customer, Mr G Gibson (Sales Ledger account GI343845) who is having his account limit increased to £55,000. He requested the increase in a letter dated 23 March.

There are eight major errors which could include wrong spellings, bad grammar or the wrong use of words.

You are to:

(a) Identify the eight incorrect words and enter them in the left-hand column of the table below.

(b) Enter your correction of these eight words on the appropriate line in the right-hand column of the table below.

Dear Mr Gibbon,

Extenson of credit limit to £50,000, Account ref GI34845

Thank you for yr letter of 23 April asking for an increase in your credit limit to £55,000.

We are pleased to advise you that we are happy to agree to this request and have carried out all the neccesary amendments to our records.

Yours faithfully,

incorrect word	correction

Task 6

Benetom Ltd is an expanding fashion clothes company.

This year it has made record sales of one and a half million pounds. Benetom operates through five regional divisions. A breakdown of the regional sales is as shown below. The calculations are not quite complete.

Division	**Sales (£)**
North West	271,790
North East	317,210
Midlands	293,000
South West & Wales	to be announced
London & South East	to be announced

(a) Calculate the total sales figure for South West & Wales and London & South East for the year.

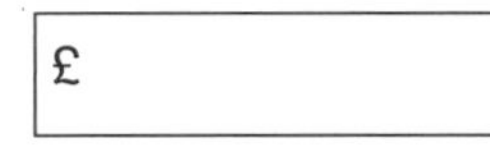

(b) The sales for London & South East were three times as great as the sales for South West & Wales.

Calculate the sales figures for these two Divisions and enter the figures in the table below.

South West & Wales	£
London & South East	£

(c) The total sales target for all divisions was £1.6 million. The North West Division was targeted to contribute 1/8 of the total sales.

Calculate the North West Division sales target and the difference between the target and the actual sales figure. If the sales are higher than target insert a '+' in front of the figure; if they are lower, insert a '–'.

North West Division sales target	£
Difference target and actual figure	£

(d) Calculate the percentage difference between the target and actual sales figure for the North West Division. Round the result to two decimal places.

(e) Calculate the average (mean) sales figure for the five divisions. (Use the formula: total sales divided by the number of Divisions.)

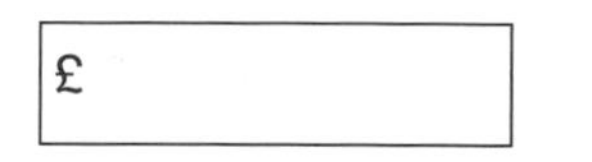

(f) Calculate the percentage difference between the average and actual sales figure for the North West Division. Round the result to the nearest whole number. If the sales are higher than the average insert a '+' in front of the figure; if they are lower, insert a '–'.

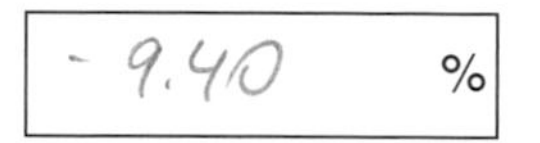

(g) The directors of Benetom are targeting a 6% rise in total sales for next year.

Calculate the amount of targeted sales in millions of pounds to two decimal places.

£

Task 7

Your manager has recently reviewed your performance and identified your strengths and weaknesses. She has suggested a number of ways in which you can improve your performance (remedying weaknesses) and develop your skills (developing your strengths).

The two areas which need special attention are:

Area 1 **A lack of organisational skills and confidence**
You are rather disorganised and have problems meeting deadlines. This largely results from a lack of confidence.

Area 2 **Foreign languages**
You are a very good linguist and it has been mentioned that you are in line for a move to the Paris office of the business.

You are to:

(a) Select the **TWO** most appropriate development activities from the list in the table below – ie **one for each** of the two development needs.

Indicate in the second column the number 1 or 2 to show which development need the chosen activity is appropriate to (Area 1 = Organisational skills, Area 2 = Foreign languages)

Enter in the far right column the likely timescale for completion of the activity. By 'timescale' it means 'when would it be best for you to complete the training?' Sooner or later? Possible completion timescales are within 3 months, 12 months, or 24 months.

Development activity	1 or 2?	Completion (months)
External time-management course (8 week)		
AAT Level 2 Certificate course – by distance learning		
External customer services 6 week short course		
In-house junior 8 weeks management course		
Short-course (10 week) basic spreadsheet training		
In-house one-day team building event - white water rafting		
French language course - evening class (10 months)		
In-house 6 month Sage computer accounting training		

(b) What does 'CPD' stand for? Tick the correct option.

	✔
Continual Professional Development	
Continuing Personal Development	
Continuing Professional Development	
Constant Personal Diversification	

Task 8

(a) There have been a number of customer complaints passed to the Accounts Manager of Nappho Limited about the level of customer service provided by the Accounts Department. The Accounts Manager therefore asked for a Report to be drafted following an online survey emailed to a sample of 55 customers.

The results of the survey are set out in the table below. A total of 25 replies were received from customers.

The areas being investigated were graded in three levels: 'Good', 'Satisfactory' and 'Unsatisfactory'.

RESULTS OF CUSTOMER SERVICE QUESTIONNAIRE (ACCOUNTS DEPARTMENT)			
Question	**Good**	**Satisfactory**	**Unsatisfactory**
How do you rate our customer service for politeness and readiness to help?	20	4	1
How well informed about our services and systems are the staff that you speak to?	12	7	6
How easy is it to get through the main switchboard to the Accounts Department?	5	8	12

Convert the figures in the above table to percentages of the total number of responses and complete the table below. Remember that there were 25 responses received.

RESULTS OF CUSTOMER SERVICE QUESTIONNAIRE (ACCOUNTS DEPARTMENT)			
Question	**Good** %	**Satisfactory** %	**Unsatisfactory** %
How do you rate our customer service for politeness and readiness to help?			
How well informed about our services and systems are the staff that you speak to?			
How easy is it to get through the main switchboard to the Accounts Department?			

Now complete Tasks 8(b), 8(c) and 8(d) which follow.

(b) Select **THREE conclusions** to be included in the Report. Tick the appropriate boxes.

	✔
The results for customer service for politeness were good	
The politeness of staff was thought to be generally less than satisfactory	
Staff knowledge of service and systems was without fault	
Staff knowledge of service and systems was at fault in a number of instances	
The switchboard worked perfectly for all the customers	
Many customers found it difficult in getting through the main switchboard to the Accounts Department	

(c) Select **TWO recommendations** to be included in the Report. Tick the appropriate boxes.

	✔
Take no action immediately but send out the questionnaire to another group of customers after six months	
Timetable training sessions for Accounts staff in order to improve their technical knowledge, and suggest they enrol for an AAT course	
Consult with the managerial staff in charge of the main company switchboard and ask that urgent action be taken to improve the service provided to customers	
Suggest that customers are encouraged to send in emails rather than use the telephone to contact the Accounts Department staff	

(d) A report normally contains seven sections:

- Summary (executive)
- Findings (main body)
- Recommendations
- Appendices
- Conclusions
- Introduction
- Title

You are to sort these sections into the order in which they will appear in the report and enter them in the table below.

1	
2	
3	
4	
5	
6	
7	

Task 9 (a)

Dissatisfaction within a team requires action. If nothing is done about the problem, the effectiveness of the team could be affected.

Sometimes problems can be sorted out personally with an individual, sometimes they will need to be referred to a Line Manager. Assume that you are an Accounts Assistant and indicate below which issues can be resolved by you, and which will need to be referred to a Line Manager.

	✔ by you	✔ by manager
A colleague has a habit of asking you to finish the invoicing when she has to go to meet her boyfriend		
Your Line Manager assumes you are trained in spreadsheets but you are not and you have problems in trying to use them		
A colleague is consistently making mistakes which reflects badly on your own work		

(b) Laura has recently joined the Sales Ledger section of the accounts team on a transfer from the Payroll section. She has been asked to stand in by the Line Manager to answer the customer queries that often come in after the statements have been sent out.

A customer calls and complains that a payment had been sent but was not showing on the statement. He is a plain speaking customer and can sound rude but Laura completely loses her temper and is very short with him. The impact of her behaviour has consequences. Tick the most accurate statement.

	✔
Laura is solely responsible so the outburst does not reflect on the team	
Laura's outburst reflects badly on her and also the Sales Ledger section of the Accounts Department	
Laura's outburst reflects badly on her, the Sales Ledger section and also the whole organisation, including the Accounts Department	

(c) You work in the Payroll section and have to check the overtime on the payslips by Friday lunchtime because they have to be distributed in the afternoon. It is just 30 minutes before your lunch when the Accounts Manager emails and asks if you can provide him as soon as possible with payroll data for an HMRC return.

What should you do? Indicate the correct option.

	✔
Ignore the email and pretend that you have not yet received it	
Reply to the email saying that you are involved in doing something urgent, but will get the figures to the Manager as soon as possible	
Refer the matter to your Line Manager, asking that a colleague could check the overtime on the payslips	
Refer the matter to your Line Manager, relying on him to make an appropriate decision	

Task 10

(a) The six descriptions in the table below describe the fundamental principles of ethics in the workplace, the names of which are:

integrity **objectivity** **equality** **professional competence and due care**

confidentiality **professional behaviour**

You are to complete the table by inserting the name of the appropriate fundamental principle in the column on the right.

Not being influenced by conflicts of interest	
Honesty, truthfulness and fair dealing	
Acting in a professional way	
Developing professional knowledge and skills	
Not discriminating against anyone in any situation	
Not disclosing information unless authorised to do so	

(b) Indicate whether the statements set out below are true or false.

Statement	**True** ✔	**False** ✔
If an employee suspects that an action he is taking involves a conflict of interest he should tell his employer about it		
Confidentiality means not revealing information held by your employer under any circumstances		
An employee buying food from a supermarket where she works is experiencing a conflict of interest		
An Accounts Assistant working in payroll who tells his friend how much his Managing Director earns is breaking confidentiality		

Task 11

(a) Identify which **FOUR** of the following are examples of a sustainability policy within an organisation.

	✔
Installing solar power panels on the work premises roof	
Keeping the lights on all the time to take advantage of cheap rate power	
Encouraging staff to take holidays in low-cost resorts in distant countries	
Encouraging staff to use emails rather than paper communications	
Choosing the cheapest suppliers for goods and services	
Using low carbon emission company cars	
Providing a free parking scheme for staff	
Organising a staff team for a marathon to raise money for famine relief	

(b) A policy of sustainability in the workplace can sometimes provide financial benefits to an organisation. Indicate in the table below the **TWO** policies which will help to increase profitability.

	✔
The legal requirement for the safe disposal of electrical and electronic equipment	
A shop charging customers 10p for plastic bags	
A business which runs a fleet of fuel-efficient cars	

Practice assessment 1 answers

Task 1

(a)

Emergency procedures for fire	✔
Quality control	
Clothing worn on the production line	
The use of environmentally friendly cleaning materials	

(b)

Only line managers have access to an organisation's policies and procedures	
Using policies and procedures helps employees to work effectively	✔
Following policies and procedures is essential for obtaining qualifications	
The law requires that there is a set of policies and procedures for payroll	

(c)

The Production Department	
The tax authorities	✔
Competitors	
The bank	✔

Task 2

(a)

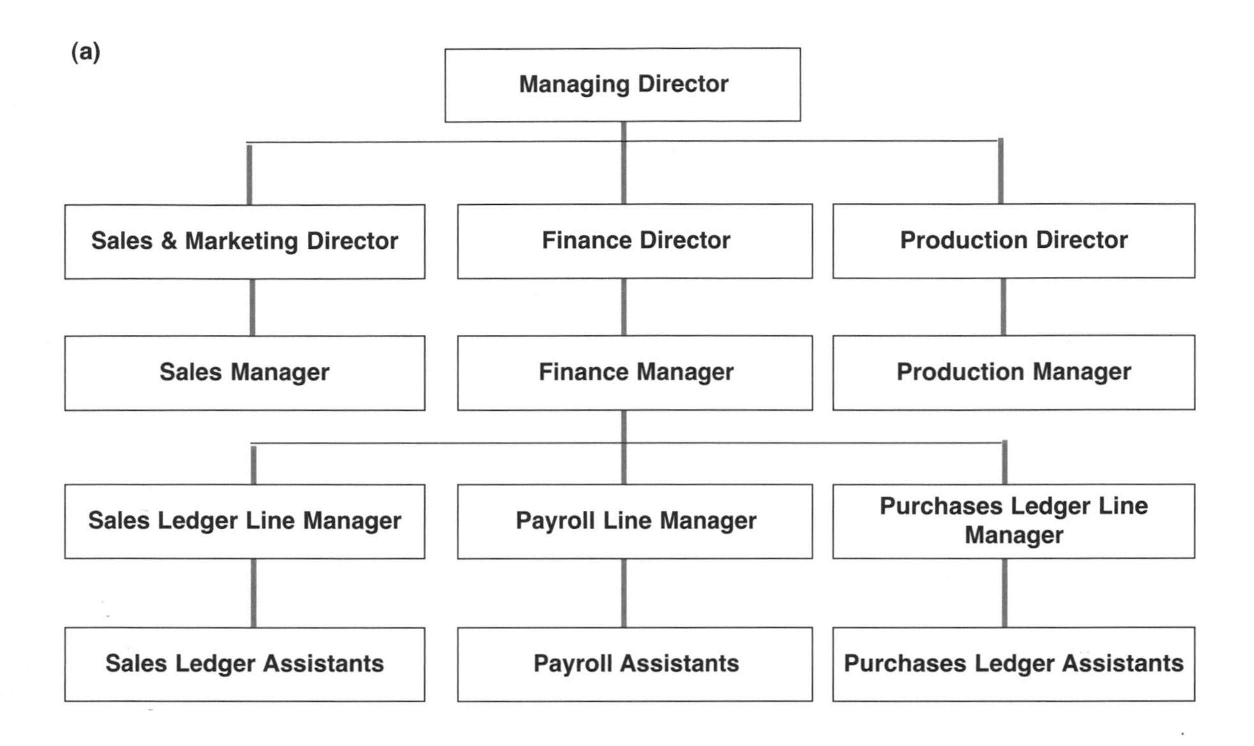

(b)

Paying into the bank once a month	
Giving customers long credit periods	
Giving customers short credit periods	✔
Paying supplier invoices as soon as they are received	
Sending chaser letters to customers who do not pay on time	✔
Using cash to pay smaller invoices	

Task 3

(a)

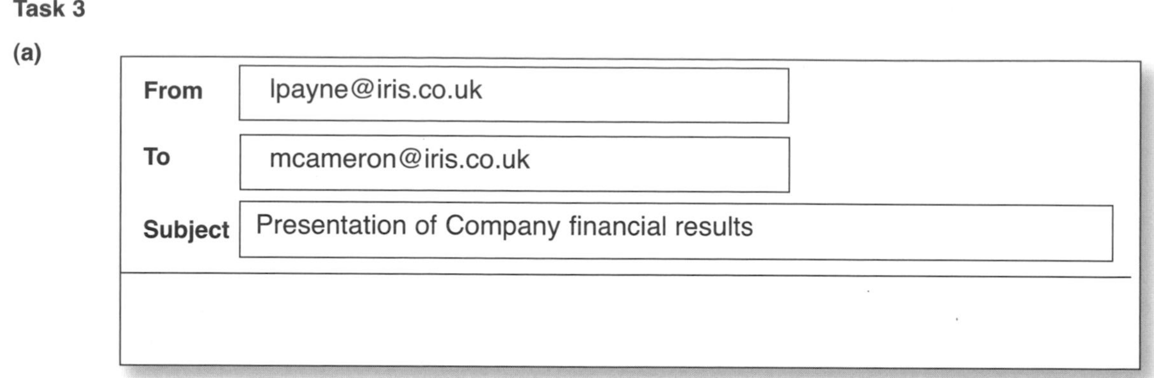

From	lpayne@iris.co.uk
To	mcameron@iris.co.uk
Subject	Presentation of Company financial results

	Paragraph 1	**Paragraph 2**
We are holding a meeting on 20 June between 11.00 and 12.00 for 40 people and will be grateful if you could arrange a suitable room for us.		
We will need projection equipment and a support technician. We will also need refreshments (coffee, tea and biscuits) to be served from 10.45. All costs are to be charged to Budget code ACC90971. Please can you let me have the details by 6 July.		
We are holding a meeting on 20 July between 11.00 and 12.30 for 40 people and will be grateful if you could arrange a suitable room for us.		
We will need projection equipment and a support technician. We will also need refreshments (coffee, tea and biscuits) to be served from 10.45. All costs are to be charged to Budget code ACC90871. Please can you let me have the details by 6 July.		✔
We will need projection equipment. We will also need refreshments (coffee, tea and biscuits) to be served from 10.45. All costs are to be charged to Budget code ACC90871. Please can you let me have the details by 6 July.		
The meeting is to be held on 20 July between 11.00 and 12.00 for 60 people and we will be grateful if you could arrange a suitable room for us.		
We are holding a meeting on 20 July between 11.00 and 12.00 for 40 people and will be grateful if you could arrange a suitable room for us.	✔	
We will need projection equipment and a support technician. We will not need refreshments on this occasion. All costs are to be charged to Budget code ACC90871. Please could you let me have all the necessary details by 6 July.		

(b)

	True	False
All emails are informal and so the punctuation can also be informal		✔
A 'CC' field on an email means that the email requires a confirmation of receipt		✔

Task 4

(a)

THURSDAY 'TO DO' LIST (in order of completion)	
Task 1	Dealing with emails and the post
Task 2	Processing sales orders
Task 3	Sales invoicing and credit notes on Sage
Task 4	Preparing and sending out customer statements
Task 5	Updating the office filing

(b)

If statements or chaser letters are sent out late this would adversely affect the cash flow of the business	✔
Processing of payments received from customers would be delayed	
The overdue account letters might not be produced on time	✔
The office filing might be delayed	
The post may not get opened	
The statements might not be produced on time	✔

Task 5

incorrect word	correction
Mr	Mrs
TOP244628	TOP24628
ammend	amend
inceased	increased
affect	effect
their	there
Your's	Yours
faithfully	sincerely

Task 6

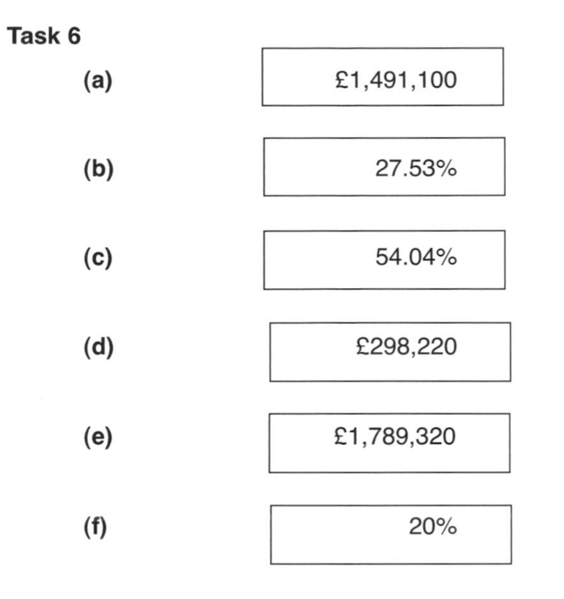

(a) £1,491,100

(b) 27.53%

(c) 54.04%

(d) £298,220

(e) £1,789,320

(f) 20%

(g) and (h)

Region	**Revised Sales (£) January - March**
South	356,400
West	349,340
North	410,520
East	374,840
Total sales	1,491,100

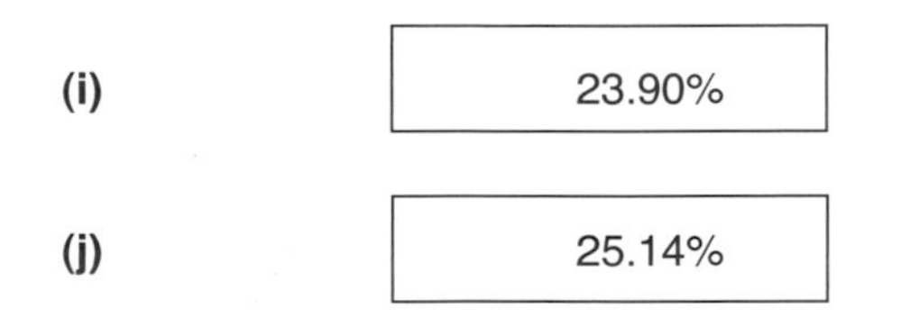

(i) 23.90%

(j) 25.14%

Task 7

(a)

Development activity	1 or 2?	Completion (months)
External time-management course (8 week)		
AAT Level 2 Certificate course – by distance learning		
External customer services 6 week short course	1	within 3 months
In-house junior 8 weeks management course		
Short-course (10 week) basic spreadsheet training		
In-house one day team building event - white water rafting		
French language course - evening class (10 months)		
In-house 6 month Sage computer accounting training	2	within 12 months

(b)

SMART objective	Sentence number
Specific	4
Measurable	5
Achievable	1
Realistic	3
Time bound	2

Task 8

(a)

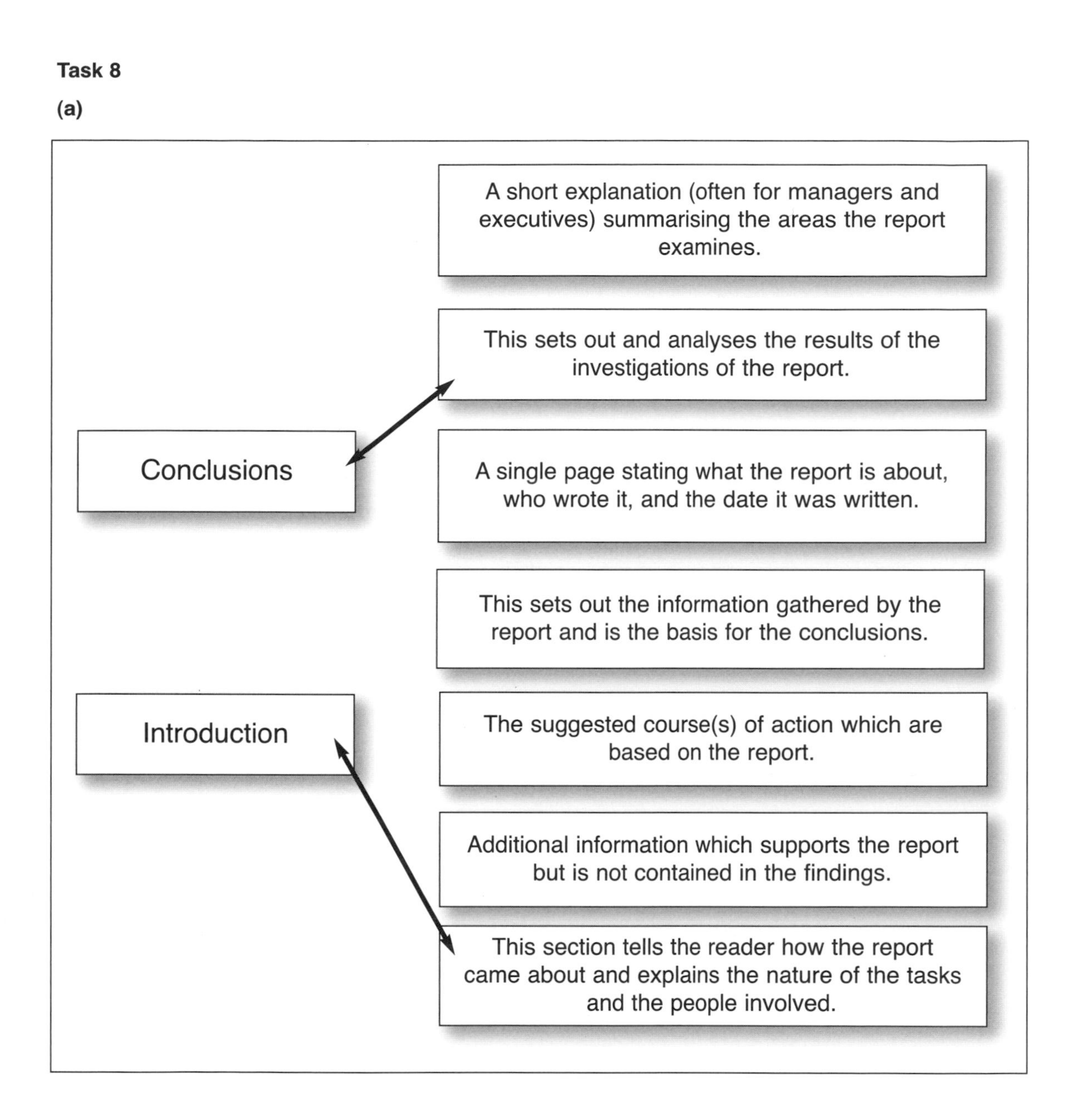
Conclusions
Introduction
A short explanation (often for managers and executives) summarising the areas the report examines.
This sets out and analyses the results of the investigations of the report.
A single page stating what the report is about, who wrote it, and the date it was written.
This sets out the information gathered by the report and is the basis for the conclusions.
The suggested course(s) of action which are based on the report.
Additional information which supports the report but is not contained in the findings.
This section tells the reader how the report came about and explains the nature of the tasks and the people involved.

Task 8 (continued)

(b)

The existing manual payroll system is the cheapest option over the three years	
The computerised payroll system is the cheapest option over the three years	✔
It would be better and cheaper in the long run to have the payroll processed by an external payroll bureau	
It would not be a good idea to use the computerised payroll option because the set-up costs are so high	
It would be a good idea to use the computerised payroll option because the set-up costs are only a 'one-off' expense and the long-term total costs are lower	✔
It would be a good idea to use the external payroll bureau because it would reduce the need for staff training	

(b)

Call a meeting of Accounts staff who work on payroll and tell them that they will be expected to work more efficiently when using the manual system	
Call a meeting of Accounts staff and explain to them the benefits using a computerised accounting system and promise them suitable training	✔
Call a staff meeting and tell the employees that the payroll will be processed by an external bureau	
Draw up a plan for the extra computer equipment that will be needed and obtain further information about computer accounting training courses	✔

Task 9

(a)

Work to a high standard, quickly, delegating tasks where possible	
Work to a high standard, within deadlines, and efficiently	✔
Work within deadlines, efficiently and letting the manager prioritise tasks	

(b) (1)

No effect because the Department has just finished its payroll run	
It could reflect badly on you because you are not helping him	
It could reflect reflect badly on the Department and also the organisation because the payroll could get delayed and employees might receive the incorrect pay	✔

(2)

Do nothing at all because you would like him to get a transfer elsewhere	
Mention the problem to your line manager if the situation does not improve	✔
Mention the problem to the Human Resources Manager	

Task 10

(a)

Effectiveness	
Efficiency	
Integrity	✔
Motivation	
Equality	✔

(b)

A local firm of accountants has been appointed by your company to undertake the annual audit of your company's accounts. They are on your premises and they are given the payroll details of all the company's employees.	
A customer calls and asks you for the telephone number of one of your colleagues, as it is an emergency. You give the customer the number.	✔
You are moved to the payroll section and notice that all the salary slips of the staff are being printed out and you can see how much the Accounts Manager earns. You mention this amount to a colleague.	✔
Your partner works in the same office as you and you discuss one of your customers over the breakfast table. Nobody else is present.	

(c)

Professional behaviour	
Objectivity	✔
Professional competence and due care	

Task 11

(a)

Sponsorship of a local school sports event	✔
Using suppliers who charge the lowest prices	
Using the cheapest paper in the photocopiers	
Financing an employee to take an AAT qualification	✔
Using suppliers who source their products from overseas	
Organising 'cycle to work' schemes	✔
Asking staff to turn out the lights at the end of the working day	✔
Setting product prices high to improve profitability	

(b)

The need for a company to support socialist political principles	
The need for a company to adopt a strategy for promoting sustainable principles	✔
A company's responsibility to provide training courses for staff which encourage staff to 'bond' and work effectively together	

Practice assessment 2 answers

Task 1

(a)

Established by the main UK professional accounting bodies	
Established by the Human Resources Department of the organisation	
Set up by the organisation itself	✔
Set out in Health and Safety law	

(b)

Grievance procedures for staff complaints	✔
Environmental policy	✔
Quality control in manufacture	
Emergency procedures for suspected letter bomb	

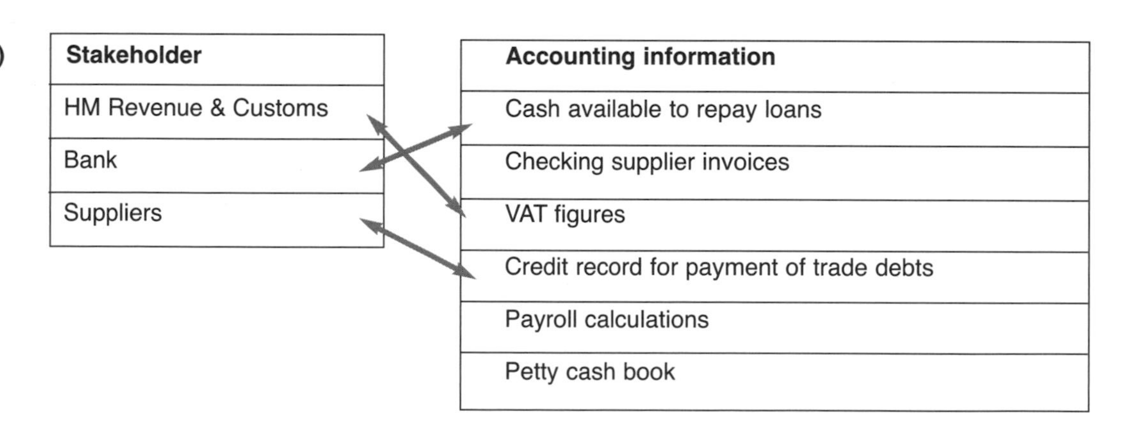

Task 2

(a)

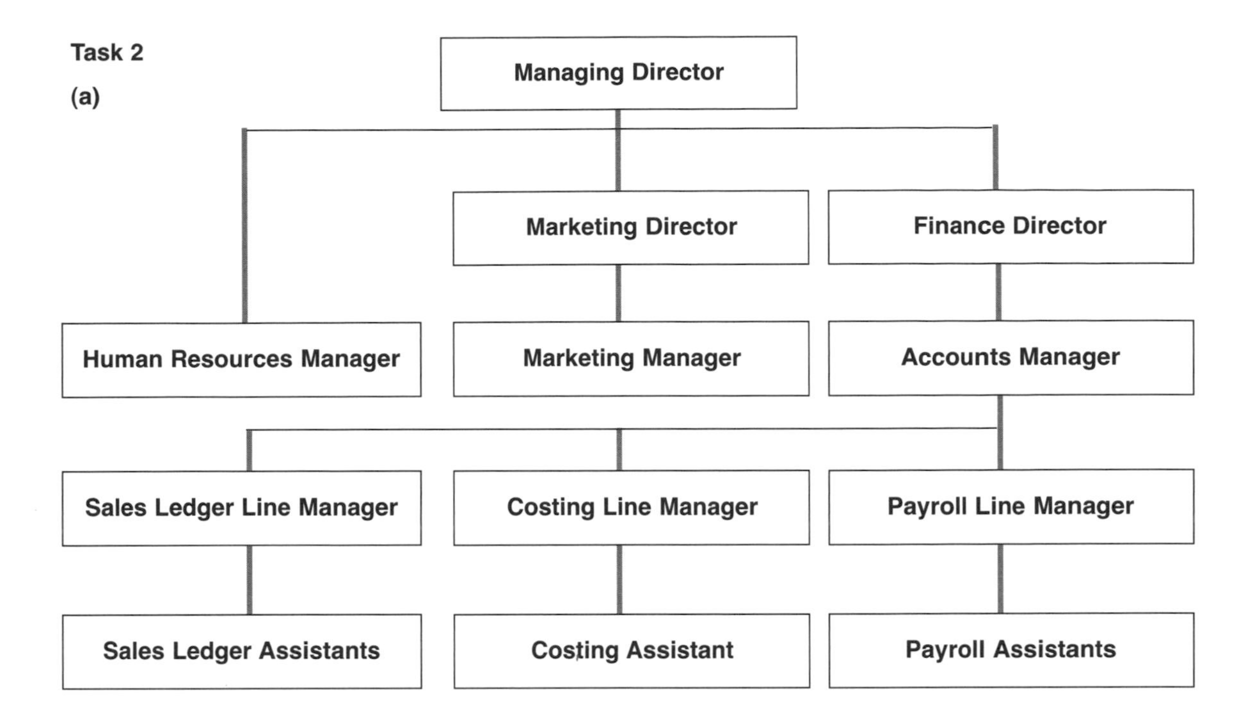

(b)

Purchases Ledger Assistants only	
Assistants in the Accounting Department only	
Assistants from a variety of Departments	✔

(c)

action	**will help solvency**	**will not help solvency**
Paying into the bank frequently	✔	
Giving customers short credit periods	✔	
Paying into the bank once a month to save petrol		✔
Paying supplier invoices later rather than sooner	✔	
Using company credit cards for staff expenses	✔	
Giving customers long credit periods		✔

Task 3

(a)

From gciambella@archo.co.uk

To jgreen@archo.co.uk

Subject March payroll data [1]

Hi Jo

Please send me the hours worked by all employees by department [2] for the month of March [3]. It would be useful if you could send me this data on the usual spreadsheet. I need the information by 5 April. [4]

Many thanks and kind regards

Gina

Payroll Section, Accounts Department

(b)

	True	False
It is normal practice when writing emails to write ALL URGENT REQUESTS IN CAPITAL LETTERS		✔
It is normal practice when writing emails to copy in all members of your own Department		✔

Task 4

(a)

Email to say that your work schedule will not allow you to do the task in time	
Reply to say that you will have the figures for him if you can do overtime on Thursday evening	
Confirm that you will have the figures for him in time for his meeting on Friday	✔
Do not reply to him but just hope that you can provide the figures in time	

(b)

FRIDAY 'TO DO' LIST (in order of completion)	
Task 1	Dealing with emails and the post
Task 2	Preparing account information for Gerda Construction Ltd
Task 3	Processing sales invoices
Task 4	Listing the cheques and cash for paying in at the bank
Task 5	Paying in at the bank

Task 5

incorrect word	**correction**
Miss	Mrs
FF287442	FF28742
£12,957.00	£12,957.50
appologise	apologise
recieved	received
what	that
adviced	advised
your	yours

Task 6

(a) 77,500

(b) 20%

(c) 40%

(d) $^1/_5$

(e) £2,310 each

(f) 19,375

(g) 1,200

(h) £2,520,000

(i) Two million, five hundred and twenty thousand pounds

Task 7(a)

Development activity	1 or 2?	Completion (months)
External time-management course (8 week)		
AAT Level 2 Certificate course – by distance learning	2	12 months
External customer services 6 week short course		
In-house junior 8 weeks management course		
Short-course (10 week) basic spreadsheet training	1	3 months
In-house one-day team building event - white water rafting		
French language course - evening class (10 months)		
In-house 6 month Sage computer accounting training		

(b)

What are my development needs now?
What are my objectives?
How can I achieve my objectives?
How well have I achieved them?

Task 8 (a)

	conclusion	recommendation
The briefing for the trial-run was not very helpful and the opinions of the staff were not respected.		
Hot desking should be discontinued in the Accounts Department.		✔
The working environment was not improved and this led to less effective working by the department.	✔	
Hot desking should be introduced in the other DirectInsure offices.		
It was beneficial not to have desks cluttered up with personal possessions.		
Staff missed being able to personalise their desks with their belongings.	✔	
Hot desking should not be introduced in the other DirectInsure offices.		✔
Hot desking had a bad effect on the levels of customer service provided.	✔	
Staff were motivated by the new system, absenteeism was reduced and fewer complaints received.		
Hot desking should be continued in the Accounts Department.		

(b)

Introduction	
Executive summary	
Appendices	✔
Main body	

Task 9

(a)

	by you	by a manager
A colleague keeps taking your crisps	✔	
A colleague keeps taking office postage stamps		✔
A colleague has bad body odour	✔	

(b)

Carry out the sales figures task for the Senior Accounts Manager, as she is more important, and paying in at the bank could always wait until another day	
Complete the credit slips for the bank and the sales figures as quickly as you can, leaving out the normal checking processes, hoping that you will be able to carry out both tasks within the set deadlines	
Discuss your workload with your Line Manager and explain that you cannot carry out both tasks within the set deadlines. He can then decide how to allocate the tasks to his staff so that both deadlines are met	✔

(c)

Members can rely on other members to complete the work on time	
Members will support colleagues and provide help when required	✔
Members complete tasks within given deadlines	✔
Members will always be able to deal with dissatisfaction without having to refer to a higher authority	

Task 10

(a)

Professional behaviour	✔
Professional competence and due care	✔
Professional responsibility	
Integrality	
Inequality	

(b)

A local firm of accountants has been appointed by your company to undertake the annual audit of your company's accounts. They are on your premises and they are given the payroll details of all the company's employees.	
A customer calls and asks you for the telephone number of one of your colleagues, as it is an emergency. You give the customer the number.	✔
You are moved to the payroll section and notice that all the salary slips of the staff are being printed out and you can see how much the Accounts Manager earns. You mention this amount to a colleague.	✔
Your partner works in the same office as you and you discuss one of your customers at home over the breakfast table. Nobody else is present.	

(c)

Professional behaviour	
Objectivity	✔
Professional competence and due care	

Task 11

(a)

Ensuring health and safety in the workplace	
Taking students from local schools on work experience schemes	✔
Avoiding conflicts of interest in the workplace	
Using suppliers who source their products from renewable resources	✔
Asking staff to turn off the computers at the end of the working day	✔
Improving sales to increase profitability	
Organising 'car-sharing' schemes for employees coming to work	✔
Installing low cost photocopiers	

(b)

Efficient use of materials, eg using both sides of paper for printing documents	✔
The use of low energy light bulbs	✔
The use of expensive packaging which is made from recycled cardboard	

Practice assessment 3 answers

Task 1

(a)

Authorisation limits for the signing of cheques	
Authorisation limits for ordering goods and services	
Setting the tax codes issued for calculating employees' pay	✔
Operation of the petty cash system	

(b)

Staff disciplinary measures	✔
Dress code for sales staff	
Use of the company logo in advertising material	
Emergency procedures for a fire alarm	✔

(c)

Shareholders	
The local community	
Suppliers	✔
Government departments	
Banks	✔

Task 2

(a)

Finance Director	✔
Sales Director	
Costing Assistant	
Payroll Manager	

(b)

Sales Manager	
Purchase Ledger Line Manager	
Payroll Line Manager	
Sales Ledger Line Manager	✔

(c)

	yes	no
Offering settlement discount to your customers	✔	
Keeping a schedule of when your customer accounts need to be paid	✔	
Giving longer credit periods to customers to encourage sales		✔
Investing surplus cash in a bank account which offers a high rate of interest but requires twelve months notice of withdrawal		✔

Task 3

(a)

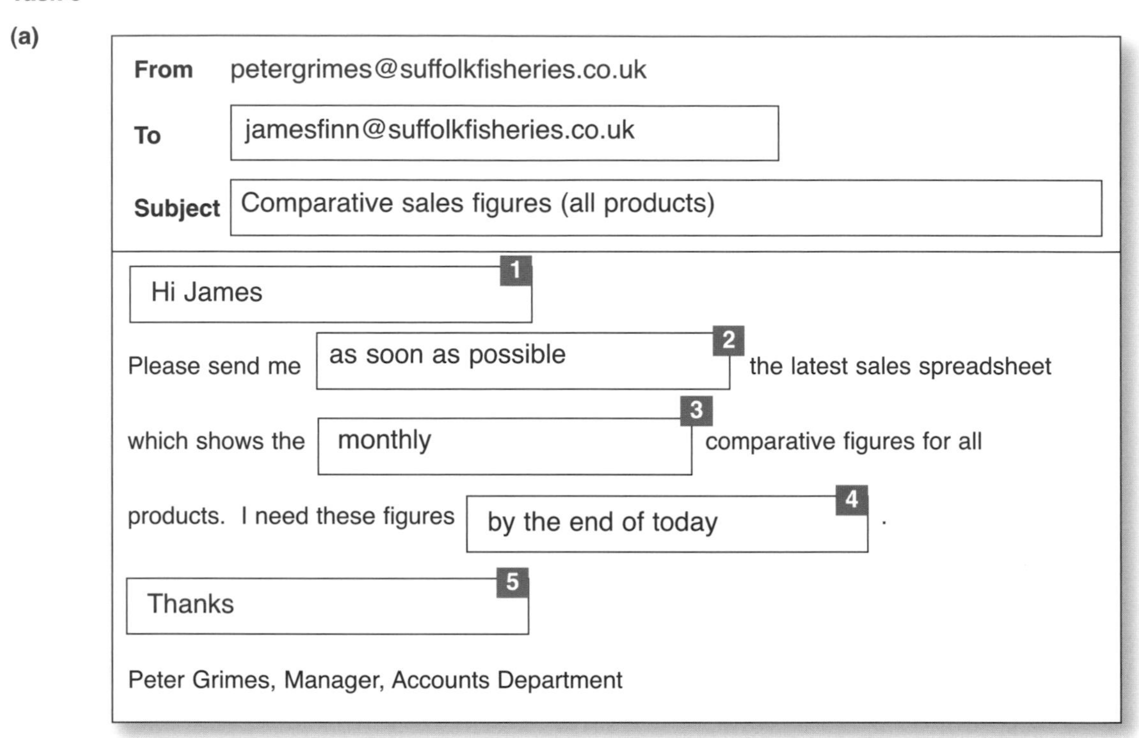

From petergrimes@suffolkfisheries.co.uk

To jamesfinn@suffolkfisheries.co.uk

Subject Comparative sales figures (all products)

1 Hi James

Please send me 2 as soon as possible the latest sales spreadsheet which shows the 3 monthly comparative figures for all products. I need these figures 4 by the end of today .

5 Thanks

Peter Grimes, Manager, Accounts Department

(b)

	True	False
The language used in an email should always be informal		✔
When writing emails it is not a good idea to use a lot of 'smileys', ie punctuation or symbols used to show a smiley face (or a sad face)	✔	

Task 4

(a)

Ask your Union representative if this is acceptable practice	
Email the Manager to ask if the appraisal could take place in a week or two when you are less busy	
Do not reply to the email because you think it is an unreasonable request	
Email the Manager to say that you will be able to attend the appraisal	✔

(b)

WEDNESDAY/THURSDAY 'TO DO' LIST (in order of completion)	
Task 1	Inventory count
Task 2	Dealing with emails and the post
Task 3	Processing purchase orders
Task 4	Processing invoices from suppliers
Task 5	Attending the appraisal interview

Task 5

incorrect word	correction
Gibbon	Gibson
Extenson	Extension
£50,000	£55,000
GI34845	GI343845
yr	your
April	March
neccesary	necessary
faithfully	sincerely

Task 6

(a) £618,000

(b) South West & Wales £154,500; London & South East £463,500

(c) North West Division sales target = £200,000

Difference target and actual figure +£71,790

(d) 35.90%

(e) £300,000

(f) –9.4%

(g) £1.59 million

Task 7(a)

Development activity	1 or 2?	Completion (months)
External time-management course (8 week)	1	3 months
AAT Level 2 Certificate course – by distance learning		
External customer services 6 week short course		
In-house junior 8 weeks management course		
Short-course (10 week) basic spreadsheet training		
In-house one-day team building event - white water rafting		
French language course - evening class (10 months)	2	12 months
In-house 6 month Sage computer accounting training		

(b)

Continual Professional Development	
Continuing Personal Development	
Continuing Professional Development	✔
Constant Personal Diversification	

Task 8 (a)

RESULTS OF CUSTOMER SERVICE QUESTIONNAIRE (ACCOUNTS DEPARTMENT)			
Question	**Good %**	**Satisfactory %**	**Unsatisfactory %**
How do you rate our customer service for politeness and readiness to help?	80	16	4
How well informed about our services and systems are the staff that you speak to?	48	28	24
How easy is it to get through the main switchboard to the Accounts Department?	20	32	48

(b) The results for customer service for politeness were good.

Staff knowledge of service and systems was at fault in a number of instances.

Many customers found it difficult in getting through the main switchboard to the Accounts Department.

(c)

Take no action immediately but send out the questionnaire to another group of customers after six months	
Timetable training sessions for Accounts staff in order to improve their technical knowledge, and suggest they enrol for an AAT course	✔
Consult with the managerial staff in charge of the main company switchboard and ask that urgent action be taken to improve the service provided to customers	✔
Suggest that customers are encouraged to send in emails rather than use the telephone to contact the Accounts Department staff	

Task 8 (d)

1	Title
2	Summary (executive)
3	Introduction
4	Findings
5	Conclusions
6	Recommendations
7	Appendices

Task 9

(a)

	by you	by manager
A colleague has a habit of asking you to finish the invoicing when she has to go to meet her boyfriend	✔	
Your line manager assumes you are trained in spreadsheets but you are not and you have problems in trying to use them		✔
A colleague is consistently making mistakes which reflects badly on your own work		✔

(b)

Laura is solely responsible so the outburst does not reflect on the team	
Laura's outburst reflects badly on her and also the Sales Ledger section of the Accounts Department	
Laura's outburst reflects badly on her, the Sales Ledger section and also the whole organisation, including the Accounts Department	✔

(c)

Ignore the email and pretend that you have not yet received it	
Reply to the email saying that you are involved in doing something urgent, but will get the figures to the Manager as soon as possible	
Refer the matter to your Line Manager, asking that a colleague should check the overtime on the payslips	
Refer the matter to your Line Manager, relying on him to make an appropriate decision	✔

Task 10

(a)

Not being influenced by conflicts of interest	**objectivity**
Honesty, truthfulness and fair dealing	**integrity**
Acting in a professional way	**professional behaviour**
Developing professional knowledge and skills	**professional competence and due care**
Not discriminating against anyone in any situation	**equality**
Not disclosing information unless authorised to do so	**confidentiality**

(b)

Statement	**True**	**False**
If an employee suspects that an action he is taking involves a conflict of interest he should tell his employer about it	✔	
Confidentiality means not revealing information held by your employer under any circumstances		✔
An employee buying food from a supermarket where she works is experiencing a conflict of interest		✔
An accounts assistant working in payroll who tells his friend how much his Managing Director earns is breaking confidentiality	✔	

Task 11

(a)

Installing solar power panels on the work premises roof	✔
Keeping the lights on all the time to take advantage of cheap rate power	
Encouraging staff to take holidays in low-cost resorts in distant countries	
Encouraging staff to use emails rather than paper communications	✔
Choosing the cheapest suppliers for goods and services	
Using low carbon emission company cars	✔
Providing a free parking scheme for staff	
Organising a staff team for a marathon to raise money for famine relief	✔

(b)

The legal requirement for the safe disposal of electrical and electronic equipment	
A shop charging customers 10p for plastic bags	✔
A business which runs a fleet of fuel-efficient cars	✔